Leonardo da Vinci

THE CODEX LEICESTER – NOTEBOOK OF A GENIUS

Leonardo da Vinci

THE CODEX LEICESTER—NOTEBOOK OF A GENIUS

POWERHOUSE PUBLISHING
PART OF THE MUSEUM OF APPLIED ARTS AND SCIENCES

First published 2000
Powerhouse Publishing, Sydney, Australia

Powerhouse Publishing
part of the Museum of Applied Arts and Sciences
PO Box K346 Haymarket NSW 1238 Australia
www.phm.gov.au
The Museum of Applied Arts and Sciences incorporates the Powerhouse Museum and Sydney Observatory.

Publication management: Julie Donaldson, Powerhouse Museum
Editing: Sue Wagner Books Pty Ltd
Cover and image design: Danny Jacobsen, Powerhouse Museum
Design: Rhys Butler
Original cover concept: Colin Rowan, Powerhouse Museum
Printing: National Capital Printing

National Library of Australia CIP
Leonard da Vinci: the Codex Leicester: notebook of a genius
Bibliography
ISBN 1 86317 081 2
1. Leonardo, da Vinci, 1452—519. Codex Hammer—Exhibitions.
500

Published in conjunction with the exhibition *Leonard da Vinci: the Codex Leicester – notebook of a genius* at the Powerhouse Museum, 5 September to 5 November 2000, an official event in the Sydney 2000 Olympic Arts Festival.

The Codex Leicester is on loan from Bill and Melinda Gates

Major sponsors

Microsoft®

NEWS LIMITED

Sponsor

Corbis

CONTENTS

FOREWORDS

Since my wife Melinda and I acquired the Codex Leicester six years ago, we have been pleased to lend it to exhibitions in major cities around the world: Venice, Milan, Rome, Paris, New York, Seattle, Lisbon, Munich, Berlin, and now Sydney. It is the fulfilment of our pledge to share Leonardo's genius with a global audience.

As the Codex Leicester has travelled throughout the world, we have been reminded of the universality of Leonardo's work. His art, his scientific observations and his prescient inventions speak to us all. They forever remain an inspiration for our own creativity and our own inquiry into the unlimited potential of technological innovation.

At the same time, we have been interested to see the individual interpretations that each city has brought to their exhibition of the Codex Leicester. In New York, the focus was on Leonardo's contributions to science. Seattle explored Leonardo's legacy in twentieth-century art and thought. The exhibition in Venice, naturally, celebrated water as the central theme of the codex and as the defining characteristic of that beautiful city.

Sydney — and specifically the Powerhouse Museum — is the first venue in which Leonardo's different interests converge. As a museum of technology, science, history and culture, the Powerhouse is an ideal context for exploring the achievements of Leonardo da Vinci. In breaking through the traditional barriers between art and science, Leonardo created a model for innovation that remains as relevant today as it was revolutionary five centuries ago.

Melinda and I are grateful for this opportunity to make the Codex Leicester accessible to the people of Australia and to all the people from around the world who are visiting Sydney during the 2000 Olympic Games. We would like to thank everyone who has worked on this project, especially the trustees, director and staff of the Powerhouse Museum. They have put together an exhibition that will delight and inspire you. We hope you enjoy it.

William H Gates III

Leonardo da Vinci reconciled the need for beauty and idealisation with the demands of a practical technology. His work is a supreme expression of human creativity and he can, in many ways, be considered a founder of the ideals that guide the Powerhouse Museum, a museum of applied arts and sciences. It is appropriate, therefore, that the exhibition *Leonardo da Vinci: the Codex Leicester — notebook of a genius* is held at a museum that reflects his divergent interests and his unique blend of science and aesthetics. The exhibition is intended to locate Leonardo's work within the broader body of knowledge found in the Powerhouse Museum and to create a dialogue between his visionary ideas for technology 500 years ago and the technological developments of today.

The impact of Leonardo's ideas has expanded well beyond his time and geography, spreading outward like the ripples in water that he measured and recorded. *Leonardo da Vinci: the Codex Leicester* is the first time that a dedicated body of Leonardo's illustrated scientific writings has been displayed in Australia. The exhibition provides a rare opportunity for Australians to view, first hand, the autograph notations of this revered artist and scientist in great depth. The Codex Leicester is a remarkable document in this respect, as the immediacy of Leonardo's handwriting and jotted, thumbnail illustrations produce almost an intimacy between writer and reader. The Codex Leicester is the most mature and systematic of Leonardo's notebooks. It deals primarily with the nature and control of water, a subject that must have a particular fascination in this, the driest of continents. The Codex Leicester provides a unique insight into how Leonardo saw and responded to nature, and also illustrates and demystifies the scientific process.

A multimedia CD-ROM guide produced by the Corbis Corporation is part of the exhibition and leads visitors through the intricacies and insights of Leonardo da Vinci's unique manuscript. The interactive program reproduces every sheet of the Codex Leicester so that it can be examined in detail and provides a synopsis of Leonardo's script. The Codescope, a unique translation tool, allows the viewer to reverse Leonardo's mirror writing and translates the Italian into contemporary English. Visitors reading Leonardo's notes will leave with a better understanding of the labyrinthine mind of one of history's great thinkers. The exhibition publication is equally helpful, carrying a lucid commentary by renowned world authority, Professor Carlo Pedretti, director of the Armand Hammer Center for Leonardo Studies at the University of California, Los Angeles.

I am most grateful to the lenders of the Codex Leicester, Bill and Melinda Gates, for allowing this precious manuscript to be displayed in Australia and selecting the Powerhouse Museum for this honour, and to Carlo Pedretti for allowing the Powerhouse Museum to use his translations. My thanks go to Fred Schroeder of Resnicow Schroeder Associates Inc, who was a sympathetic intermediary during the negotiations; Jim Spigelman, the immediate past president of the Powerhouse Museum's Board of Trustees, who initiated the loan of the Codex Leicester; and to Terence Measham AM, the former director of the Powerhouse Museum, who secured its display at the Powerhouse. In addition, I am grateful to our major sponsors, Microsoft and News Limited, and our sponsors the Corbis Corporation. Their goodwill and generous support has ensured the success of this exhibition.

Dr Kevin Fewster
Director
Powerhouse Museum

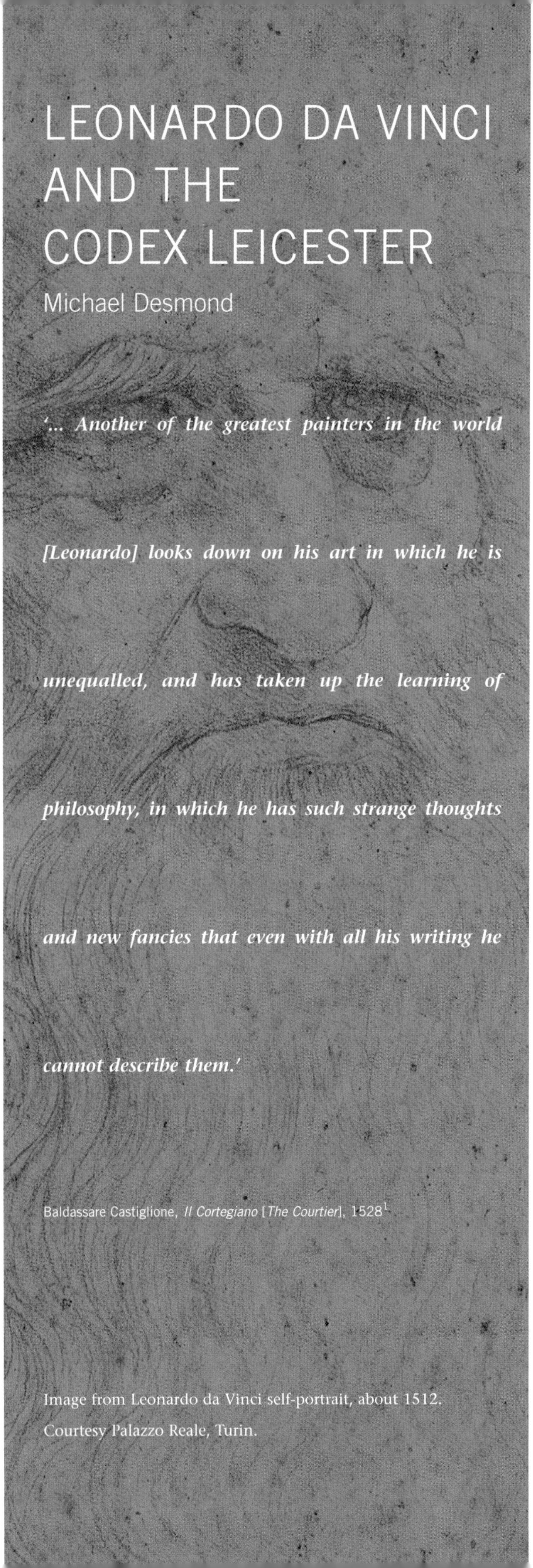

LEONARDO DA VINCI AND THE CODEX LEICESTER

Michael Desmond

'... Another of the greatest painters in the world [Leonardo] looks down on his art in which he is unequalled, and has taken up the learning of philosophy, in which he has such strange thoughts and new fancies that even with all his writing he cannot describe them.'

Baldassare Castiglione, *Il Cortegiano* [*The Courtier*], 1528[1]

Image from Leonardo da Vinci self-portrait, about 1512. Courtesy Palazzo Reale, Turin.

If anyone fits the description 'Renaissance man' it is Leonardo da Vinci. He was an engineer, architect, designer, inventor, painter and sculptor. He is best known as an artist, the man who painted the *Mona Lisa*, and it is something of a surprise to find out that Leonardo actually spent more time on scientific projects than on painting. While there are as few as fifteen paintings securely attributed to Leonardo, there are copious drawings and notes documenting his other interests. For much of his life, Leonardo conscientiously recorded his observations of nature, illustrated anatomical dissections, prepared studies for paintings, made diagrams of machine parts, listed books he owned or intended to read, itemised money owed and catalogued his ambitious plans for projects in a variety of fields. In many ways Leonardo's notebooks are as important as his paintings, and they are responsible for his status as the world's most famous polymath.

For Leonardo, art and science were inseparable. His giant figure straddles the early histories of Western art and science and he is the only person accorded a prominent place in both disciplines.

Leonardo da Vinci was born into a world of change. From the beginning of the 15th century a great change was taking place in society and altering the culture of Italy. As it evolved it came to be called the Renaissance, the 'rebirth', because of the rediscovery of ancient Roman literature and art during the period. Just as important was the resurgence of technical activity as Italian engineers and architects attempted to restore and eventually surpass the technological achievements of the past. The language of science was revitalised. Mathematics became an effective scientific tool with the introduction of Indo-Arabic numerals, including the innovative zero, into Europe via Spain during Muslim occupation. Ironically the

Muslim presence in Europe ended when the last Moorish king in Europe, Boabdil, was driven out of Granada in 1492, the year Columbus reached the Americas. Effective mathematics made scientific research possible. And better technology was the result of the application of science. Discoveries made during the Renaissance had a leapfrog effect, with one advance prompting the next in another field. The increasing sophistication of scientific discovery made for specialisation and the eventual establishment of science as a discrete area of knowledge.

Leonardo occupies an important position in the evolution of science and art, two different systems for seeing and understanding our environment. He lived at a time when many of the ways in which we now categorise and analyse the world around us were being formed. He could be seen as the meeting point for what are now two parallel streams, just as the Renaissance was a meeting point between medieval philosophies and modern science. Medieval science was characterised by ultimate and absolute truths; these were endorsed by God and the church, and were not subject to modification. Modern science regards knowledge as provisional, since it might eventually be superseded by new discoveries.

We think of Leonardo as a lone genius, totally original and exceptional. However, he was not unique in his questioning intellect, but was very much part of his time. Leonardo grew from the fertile soil of the Renaissance, nurtured by the new thoughts and ideas that were sweeping Europe, as well as the old knowledge that was being revived from classical texts. Thinkers and practitioners of the Renaissance were inspired by the tradition of ancient skills and encouraged by the examples of Roman engineering and architecture on a grand scale that survived around them. The aqueducts that fed the fountains of ancient Rome, still working, drew water supplies from 50 kilometres away. Buildings like the Pantheon and the Colosseum remained unsurpassed since their erection more than 1300 years earlier.

Leonardo appeared at a time of transition between the waning of the Middle Ages and the emerging Renaissance. He characterises the spirit of inquiry that was to create modern science, but he retained many of the principles of medieval thought. His was an impressive intellect, yet he shared the concerns and problems that challenged his contemporaries and he was distinguished from his fellows only by degree. In his complexity and contradictory outlook he epitomises this rich period.

Born in 1452 in Vinci, a small hill town in Tuscany near Florence, Leonardo was the illegitimate son of a local notary, Ser Piero, and a peasant girl, Caterina. The boy was brought up by his father's family and received a rudimentary education, but he was not eligible to enter professions such as medicine or law, so when he was about 15 his father apprenticed him to Andrea del Verrocchio, the most renowned sculptor in Florence. There the young man learnt about painting, sculpture and metal casting, perspective, architecture and anatomy, and made studies after nature. Several writers have commented on this, Vasari claiming Leonardo 'practised not one branch of art only, but all those in which drawing plays a part; … he not only worked in sculpture … but in architecture also … and he was the first, although but young, who suggested reducing the River Arno to a navigable canal from Pisa to Florence. He made designs of flour mills, and engines that might be driven by the force of water, but he wished his profession should be painting.'[2]

Left: Illustration of the moon during its crescent phase lit by 'earthlight'. Detail from the Codex Leicester, Sheet 2A, folio 2r.

Right: Rays of sunlight reflected off the watery surface of the moon, shown here with scalloped edge. Detail from the Codex Leicester, Sheet 1A, folio 1r.

Leonardo's brilliance soon equalled, then eclipsed, that of his master. In 1472 Leonardo was responsible for painting the kneeling angel on the left, and the first of his signature fantasy landscapes behind it, in Verrocchio's *Baptism of Christ*. He began painting the magnificent *Adoration of the magi* in 1481, a tour de force demonstration of his mastery of perspective, but abandoned it unfinished as he would so many other projects.

In 1482 the 29-year-old Leonardo left Florence for Milan, having offered his services to Ludovico Sforza, duke of Milan, as an engineer and painter. In his letter to the duke, Leonardo advertised himself as a military engineer, capable in many fields in times of war. Only in the last few lines of the letter did he add a proposal for a monumental equestrian sculpture of Francesco Sforza, the duke's father, noting, almost as afterthought, that he was 'a painter the equal of all others in times of peace'.[3] In Milan he painted masterworks the *Madonna of the rocks* and the *Last supper*, but spent more time on other pursuits. Leonardo designed for the duke weapons such as a giant crossbow, a scythed chariot and an 'unattackable covered wagon', a prototype for the tank, though he hated war, declaring it a 'bestial madness'. In the Codex Leicester he describes devices to swim underwater, but given '… the evil nature of men, who would use them as a means of destruction at the bottom of the sea', withholds details of the inventions. In fact, the weapons were flamboyant rather than practical, and the duke profited more from Leonardo's designs of costumes and sets for the court's theatrical wedding pageants.

It is possible that Leonardo's fascination with astronomy began with such a production. In 1490 at Sforza's request, Leonardo created an elaborate stage set for a production of *Festa del paradiso* as part of the festivities to celebrate the marriage between the duke's nephew, Gian Galeazzo, and Isabella of Aragon. Leonardo's design had the 12 signs of the zodiac arrayed around the walls, lit by multiple lights in the ceiling

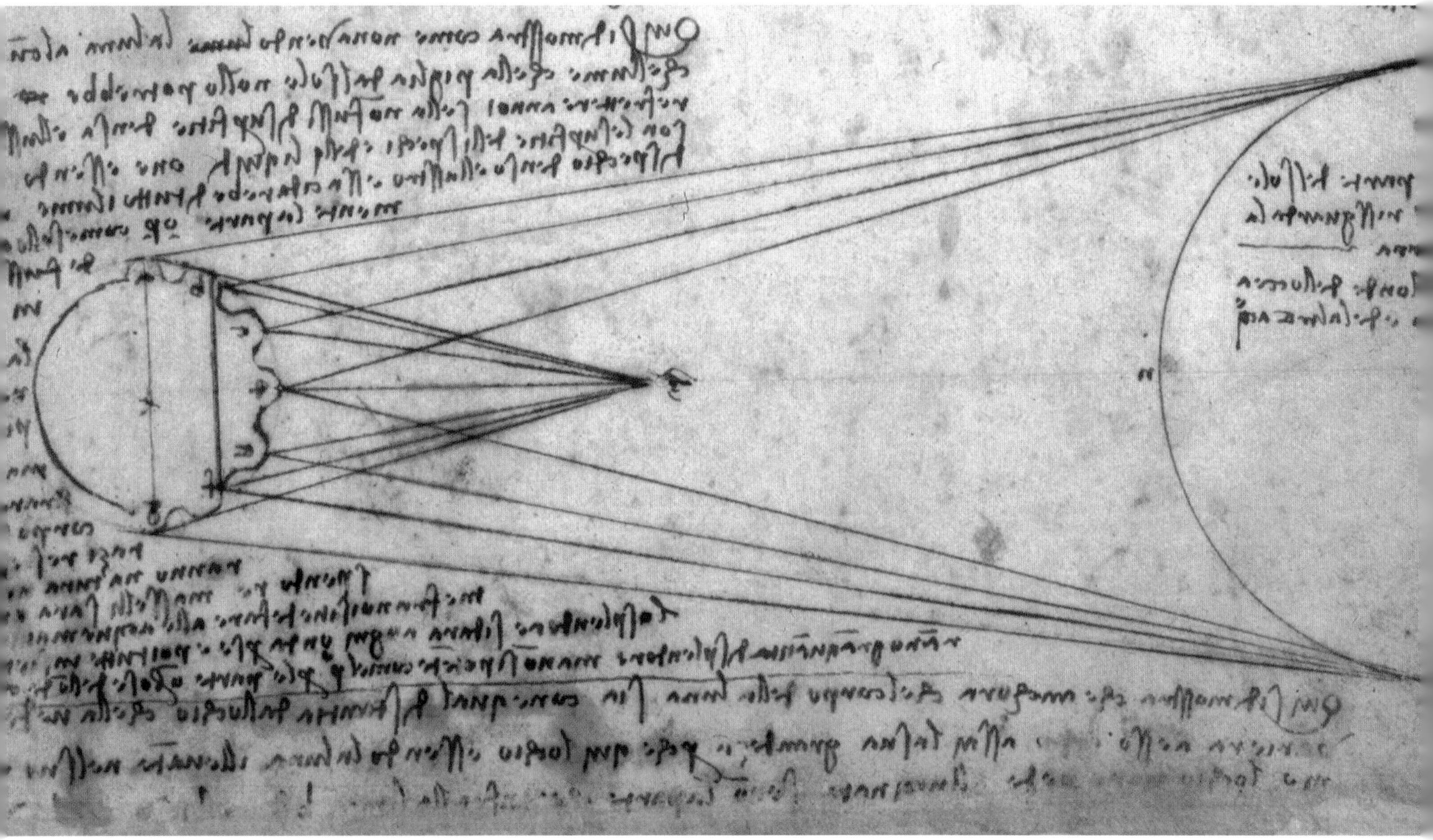

representing the stars, all of this as a fantastic backdrop to an animated planetary system comprising the sun, the moon and the the five known planets (following the then generally accepted Aristotelian model with the earth at the centre). It was driven by machinery made to his specifications.

Leonardo was to devote himself to a serious study of astronomy in his later years, noting that 'the sun does not move' and that the 'earth is not the centre of the circuit of the sun, nor in the centre of the universe'. It was after Leonardo's death that Polish astronomer Nicolaus Copernicus, in his great book *On the revolutions of the celestial spheres* published in 1543, determined instead that the planets revolve around the sun. The news was not welcomed by the Catholic church and indeed, nearly a century later, Galileo Galilei was put under house arrest for espousing Copernican theory. Leonardo's mirror writing may well have served to shield such radical ideas from the wrong eyes.

Leonardo's observations of the moon in the Codex Leicester are equally acute. He understood why moonlight was fainter than sunlight — it was generally accepted at that time that the moon did not generate light independently but reflected the sun's light back to earth. Yet if the bright illumination was reflected sunlight, why was the whole lunar disc occasionally visible when the moon was waning to a crescent? Leonardo accurately deduced that light was being reflected from the earth onto the moon's dark surface. A beautiful sketch in the Codex Leicester illustrates his theory. Leonardo's research was not published, however, and in 1610 the astronomer Johannes Kepler credited his teacher Michael Mastlin with the discovery.

Leonardo could be dramatically wrong, too. He determined that for the moon to reflect sunlight so well, it had to have a smooth reflective surface, and considered alabaster or crystal as possibilities. However from his observations of shiny globes he knew that such material would reflect light

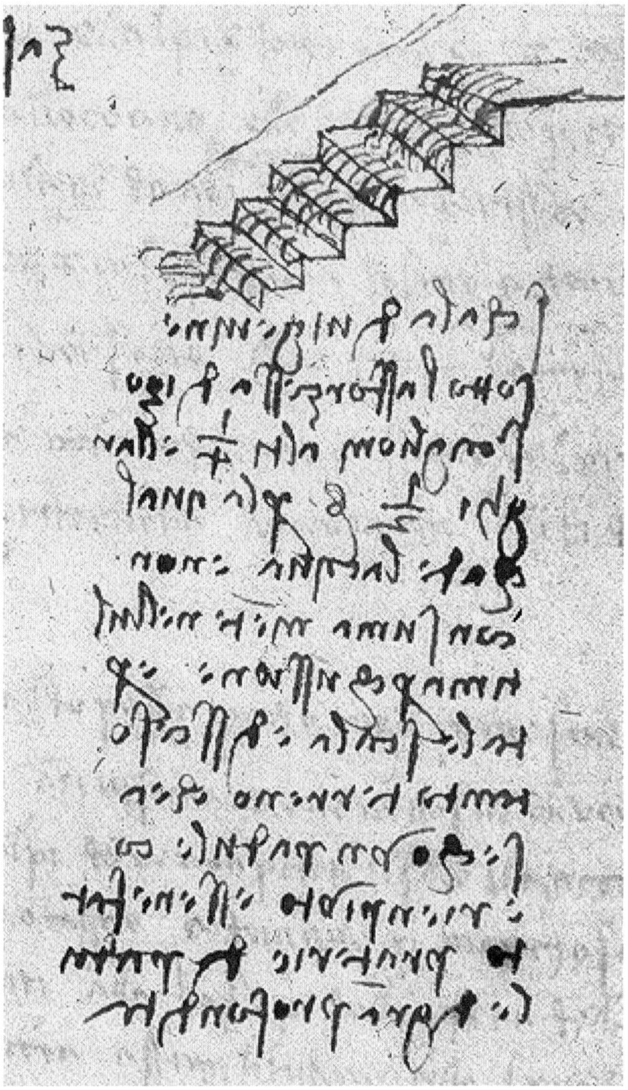

Drawing of water steps at La Sforzesca, the duke of Milan's model farm. Details from the Codex Leicester, *above* Sheet 5B, folio 32r; *right* Sheet 15B, folio 22r.

as a single intense point, unlike the variegated lunar disc that the eye could see. Rippling water would reflect light in such a way, though, and he argued for a water-covered moon. His diagrams show a scalloped lunar surface (representing a schematic watery topography) reflecting light rays.

During his ten years in Milan Leonardo made countless sketches of horses and riders for the monument to Francesco Sforza. In many ways the Sforza monument was intended to surpass the efforts of his predecessors Donatello and Verrocchio, whose magnificent portraits of the two condottieri (mercenaries) *Gattamelata* and *Colleoni* respectively were the first major equestrian statues made since Roman times. According to scholar and mathematician Luca Pacioli, the Sforza monument, at roughly 7 metres, was nearly double the height of Verrocchio's sculpture. A preliminary model in clay was exhibited in 1493, but it was never cast as the threat of invasion by the king of France, Louis XII, caused the stocks of bronze to be diverted to the production of armaments. The French invaders took Milan in 1499 and used Leonardo's model for target practice.

Many of the sketches in his notebooks address the considerable problems of casting this titanic sculpture in bronze. It is difficult to determine which of the studies of horses are intended to further the sculpture and which were pure research into equine anatomy; and equally, whether his plans for casting were for purely practical purposes or to develop an independent science of metallurgy.

Leonardo's routine of drawing developed during his stay in Milan. The earliest sketches were studies for the colossal equestrian sculpture commissioned by the duke but, as time passed, the notebooks were filled increasingly with Leonardo's ideas for military machines and intricately geared devices for lifting, as his enthusiasm inclined towards scientific studies. To the cost of his art-making, the notebooks were to preoccupy him for the rest of his life.

For his notebooks, Leonardo envisaged four major themes: a treatise on the science of painting, a treatise on architecture, a book on the elements of mechanics, and a general work on human anatomy. To these themes were eventually added notes on his studies of botany, geology, hydrology and flight. His intent was to synthesise all of his investigations with a unified world view based on his perceptions. 'All our knowledge,' he wrote, 'has its origins in our perceptions.' Leonardo believed that true knowledge derived from scientific observation, not from philosophical speculations.

With the French in control of Lombardy, Leonardo left Milan, travelling through Mantua to Venice, where he consulted on architecture, presenting the duke of Mantua with his designs for the house of the merchant Angelo de Tovaglia. As military engineer for Cesare Borgia from 1502 to 1503, he inspected and planned fortifications. After his service to the Borgias, Leonardo returned to Florence. It was between 1503 and 1506 that he was at his most influential, with many followers and numerous commissions including a request by the Signoria, the governing body of Florence, for a mural. The painting was to depict the Battle of Anghiari, but the real contest was to be an aesthetic one, as another Florentine, Michaelangelo Buonarroti, had been commissioned to produce a companion mural. In the end, neither artist went beyond making preliminary cartoons. At the height of his powers now, Leonardo was prepared to tackle ambitious engineering projects, attending the siege of Pisa to study the possibility of diverting the river Arno and designing a monumental bridge over the Bosphorus for the Turkish sultan Bajazet II. He painted the *Mona Lisa* at this time.

In 1506 Leonardo returned to Milan and devoted much of his time to scientific studies, making the notes that are now known as the Codex Leicester. In 1512 he left Milan again, and from 1513 to 1516 was in Rome. Here he came into contact with Michelangelo and Raphael, both artists working on vast papal commissions. At the request of Giuliano de' Medici, agent to Pope Leo X, Leonardo made many studies for draining the Pontine Marshes.

Without a regular patron, Leonardo eventually accepted an invitation from the French king, François I, and moved to the castle of Cloux, near Amboise in the Loire region of France, where he stayed with his faithful pupil Francesco Melzi until the end of his life. Leonardo died on 2 May 1519 in Cloux and was buried in Amboise. At the time of his death he was described as a painter, inventor and architect.

Studies of water flow around an obstacle. Details from the Codex Leicester, *above* Sheet 14A, folio 14r; *right* Sheet 15B, folio 22r.

THE CODEX LEICESTER

The Codex Leicester was written in Milan between 1506 and 1510, when Leonardo was in his mid 50s. It is written in sepia ink on 18 loose, double-sided sheets of linen paper, each folded, to make a total of 72 pages. The text is written in 'mirror writing', starting at the right-hand side of the page and finishing at the left with the letters reversed so that a page can be read normally only when held up to a mirror. It is likely that Leonardo adopted this backwards script because he was left-handed. For 'south-paws' like Leonardo, writing from left to right smudges newly inked lettering. There is some speculation that he intended to make it harder for others to read his notes and plagiarise his ideas. It is known that he intended to publish the contents of his notebooks, so the exact reason for using mirror writing remains uncertain.

Originally loose leaf, the codex was like an open file so that Leonardo could add to it at any time. It was likely that he intended these notes as the starting point for a publication, since Leonardo addresses comments to 'the reader' in several places. In earlier work (Manuscript A, circa 1490–92) Leonardo refers to his ambition to create a 'treatise on water' that would be a compendium of his theoretical and practical studies. It is possible that his notes in the Codex Leicester were intended as a guide to hydraulic technology.

The Codex Leicester is the only manuscript that deals almost exclusively with science. It is a working record of cases, observations and experiments, covering a variety of topics from astronomy to hydraulics, with water as the primary subject. During his years in Milan, Leonardo had taught himself about the waterways that linked the city to the lakes and rivers of northern Italy. He studied the canal system with its numerous locks and gates, making many detailed drawings. As a hydraulic engineer Leonardo had to learn the essential laws of water in order to harness its power. The flow of water fascinated him. He made plans for water-powered machinery, proposed draining the swamps around Milan, and spent much time studying the rippling motion, eddies and whirlpools of watercourses. The Codex Leicester describes Leonardo's methods for halting erosion, changing the course of rivers and building better bridges.

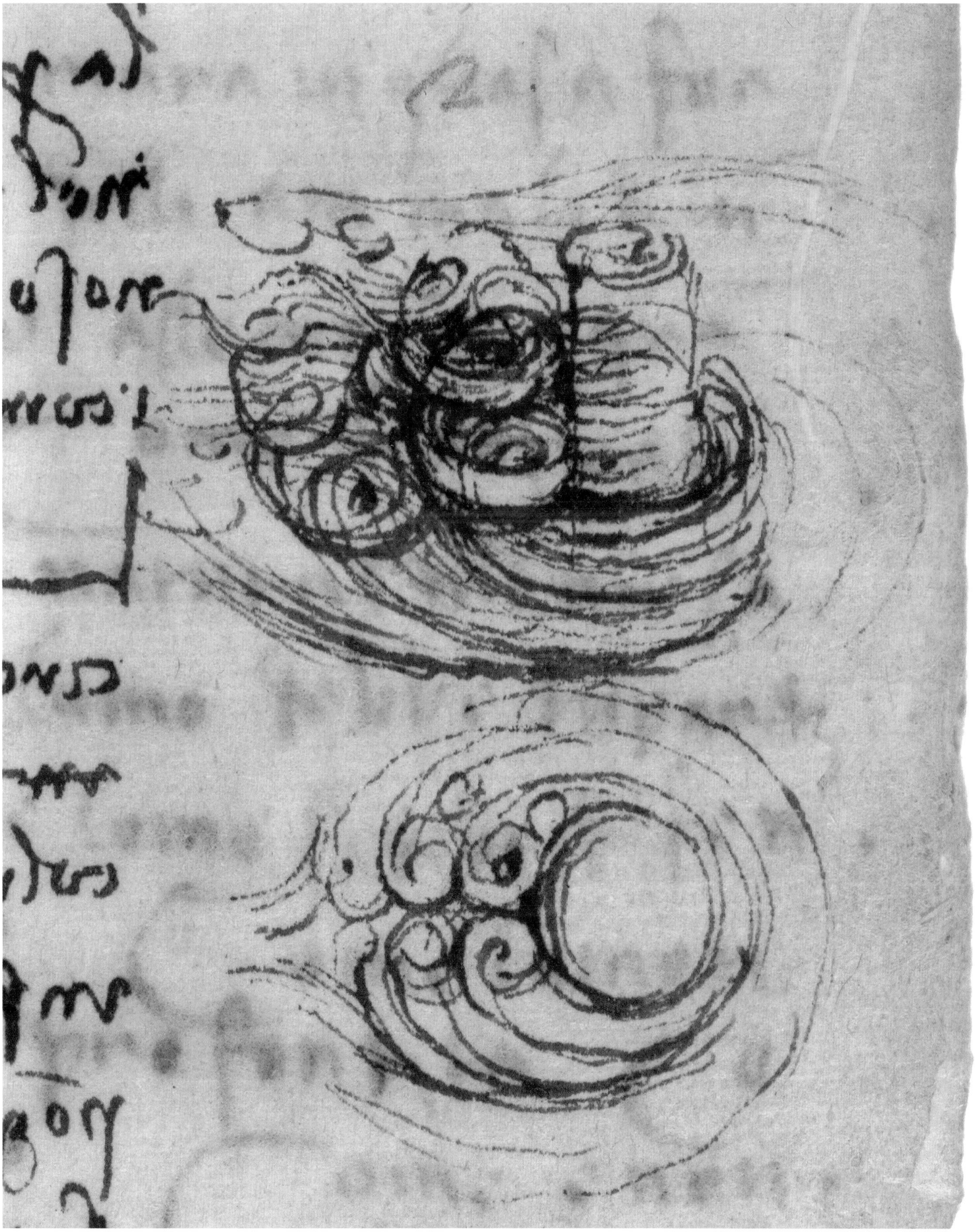

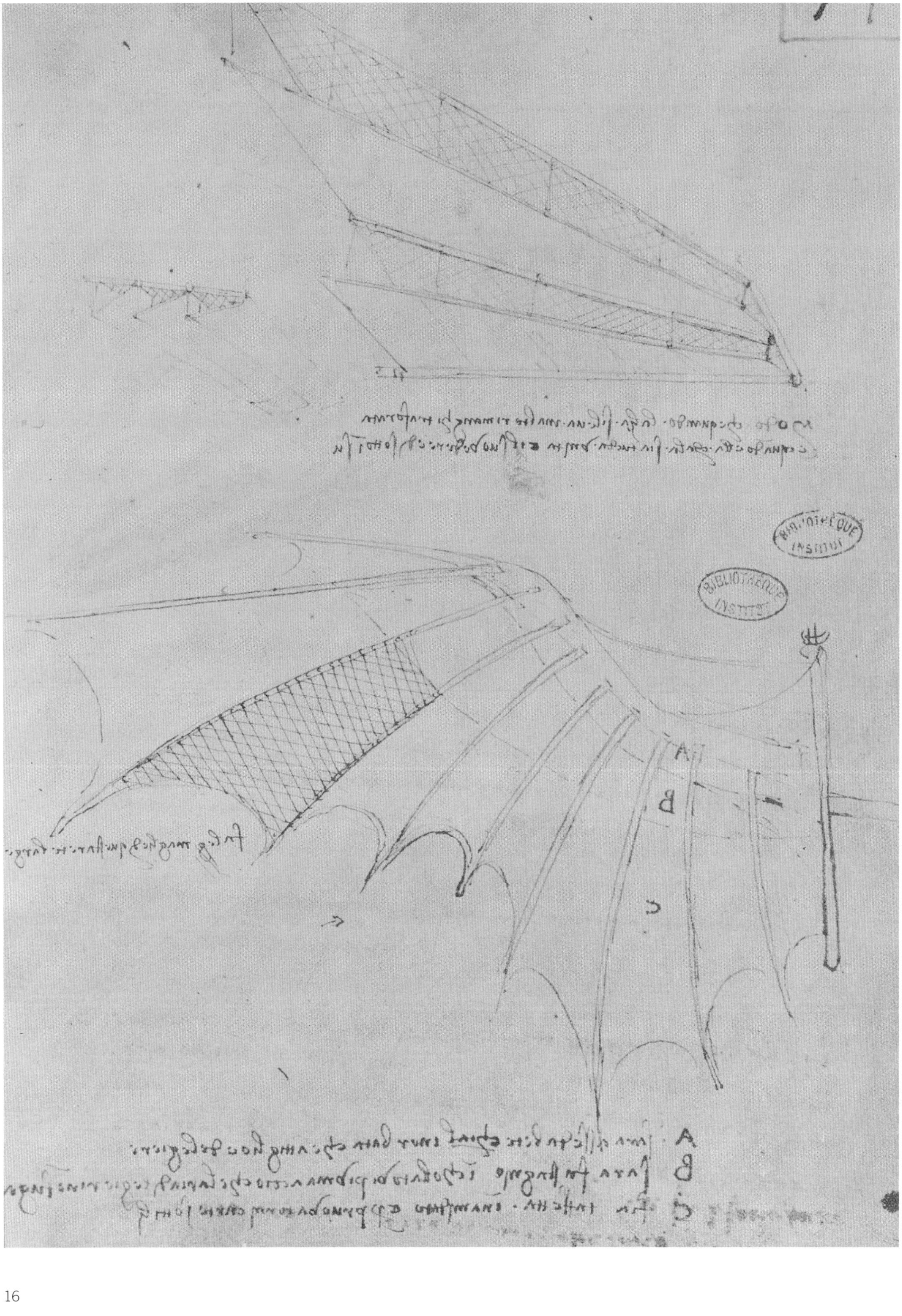
A
B
C
BIBLIOTHEQUE INSTITUT

Leonardo makes his points with a series of observations, arguments and case histories, often accompanied by thumbnail images. Well aware of the power of water to carry away earth, he reproduces a diagram of the water stairs, still in use today, that he designed in 1494 to control erosion at La Sforzesca, the duke of Milan's model farm. The steps were designed to drain the marshlands and keep the meadows green. The force of the stream is minimised by breaking the fall at regular intervals as it travels downstream.

Leonardo was interested in controlling the flow and direction of water current. Louis XII, king of France, gave Leonardo permission to use part of the Naviglio Grande Canal in Milan for his experiments. Leonardo designed different-shaped obstacles to determine the effect of each form. He writes: 'If an obstacle inclines extensively towards the oncoming waters, and is upright on its sides and back, then being washed over by waves the river will not remove soil from in front of it but on the sides and at the back it will. And if an obstacle is upright in front and inclines at the back, the water washing over it will produce a great concavity in front of it and not at the back.'[4]

Leonardo's lively mind often skipped to other subjects. On one page of the Codex Leicester he moves from a discussion of dams to an exploration of light from the moon. In a number of fascinating 'case studies', he examines why the sky is blue, how fossil seashells come to be found on mountains and expounds on his belief that the earth is a dynamic living entity — the equivalent of what today is termed 'Gaia' and popularised by James Lovelock during the 1980s.[5]

The Codex Leicester was part of the bequest Leonardo made in his will to his faithful pupil Francesco Melzi. Subsequently it was known to belong to the Milanese sculptor Guglielmo della Porta before coming into the possession of painter Giuseppe Ghezzi in 1690. Ghezzi sold the manuscript in 1717 to Englishman Thomas Coke, later Earl of Leicester, and the family, whose name the codex carries, retained the manuscript until 1980. It was then sold at auction to American businessman and collector Armand Hammer, who renamed it the Codex Hammer. In 1994 after Hammer's death it was auctioned a second time, and was purchased at a record price by Microsoft chairman Bill Gates and his wife Melinda. They restored the name Codex Leicester to the manuscript.

Above: Model of Lawrence Hargrave on his box kite. Hargrave (1850–1915), explorer, astronomer, amateur historian and inventor, was something of an Antipodean 'Renaissance man'. He invented flotation shoes for walking on water that follow the same principles as those designed by Leonardo da Vinci, and is remembered as a man who, like Leonardo, was fascinated by the possibility of human flight. He was the inventor of the box kite which, with its improved lift-to-drag ratio, opened the way for the development of the first generation of aeroplanes. On 12 November 1894, using a construction of four linked kites, he was able to fly for a short time. A number of Hargrave's models and his archival papers are held in the Powerhouse Museum.

Left: Leonardo's study for a flying machine. Manuscript B (IFP) folio 74v Institut de France, Paris.

Courtesy Institut de France, Paris

LEONARDO DA VINCI TODAY

Contemporary academics have rehabilitated the Middle Ages, reassessing the period from the decline of the Roman Empire to the 14th century, seeing it less as the Dark Ages and more as a period of gestation for what was to follow. There were many achievements in those centuries, but these were ignored in order to throw the advances of the Renaissance into higher relief.

In re-evaluating Leonardo da Vinci's work, his context and his sources, historians have determined that Leonardo was not as isolated or as uniquely original as was first thought. Many of the devices in his notebooks, previously assumed to be his own inventions, were in common use during the early Renaissance and had an established history of use. These mechanisms were not personal discoveries but factual recordings of current technology. Leonardo built up his knowledge base by seeking out and documenting existing machines. His gift was to analyse, then improve, often by combining parts from other devices.

Leonardo borrowed freely from his contemporaries, as did other Renaissance scientists and artists. It does not diminish Leonardo's status to learn that he incorporated and absorbed the work of others. His scrutiny of nature gave him a solid education and his accurate perceptions and original thought make Leonardo's interpretations enormously interesting. Leonardo's systematic exploitation of experimental method is without precedent and he deserves the accolade of 'genius'. Leonardo reconciled the need for beauty and idealisation with the demands of a functional technology. His work is a supreme expression of human creativity.

Today Leonardo da Vinci is appreciated as a figure who combined the practical and the visionary. But that hasn't always been the case. Always revered as a painter, Leonardo's contribution to science was well understood during his lifetime but overlooked after his death, as the achievements of practitioners such as Copernicus, Galileo and Sir Isaac Newton established the canon. His gifts as a scientist and engineer were rediscovered in the late 19th century, and became widely known when drawings and diagrams from his notebooks were published, revealing the broad range of his interests. Leonardo's particular genius served as a useful symbol of the reconciliation of art and science, at a time when it was believed that craftsmanship and design were being lost to the demands of industrial production.

The Great Exhibition held at the Crystal Palace in London in 1851 was more than a showcase of industrial products and crafts from the Empire: it became the focus for the linking of art and industry, as design. The complementary aims of the Arts and Crafts Movement, to preserve the beauty of traditional crafts, were born at this time as well. A host of international exhibitions followed the Great Exhibition, showing contemporary art and craft, science, inventions and manufactured goods. In response, a new kind of museum was created, embracing applied and industrial design. The Victoria and Albert Museum was established in London in 1852, the Oesterreichische Museum fur Kunst and Industrie in Vienna in 1864 and the Industrie–Museum in Cologne in 1868, for example. The 1879 International Exhibition at the Garden Palace in Sydney, in turn, inaugurated what became known as the Museum of Applied Arts and Sciences, today known as the Powerhouse Museum.

These new museums were intended to encourage good design that would bridge the gap between handicraft and manufacturing. In this climate it was reassuring to consider the example of Leonardo, forward-looking engineer and aesthete, as a paradigm. It was also apparent by the middle of the 19th century that the process of industrialisation demanded a high degree of specialisation in many particular areas, potentially creating a generation of individuals with narrow expertise. This gave additional allure to the idea of Leonardo as a 'whole' man, embodying mastery of a broad range of skills.

Leonardo's art mirrors the aesthetic development of his time, but he was some what out of step in many ways. There is a strangeness, a mystery about him that is reflected in his paintings. The enigmatic mood, the androgynous figures and grotesques in his art, today are interpreted as almost surrealist tendencies; they fascinate contemporary taste. In contrast to the equivocal atmosphere of his paintings, Leonardo's drawings of anatomy, machinery and nature are models of precision and clarity. Such contradictions establish a fuller portrait of the man.

Many of Leonardo's most ambitious projects were abandoned unfinished, and others lacked the technical support needed to complete them. A number of writers have commented on this, Vasari claiming that Leonardo 'began many works, none of which he completed, since he felt that his hand could not reach the artistic perfection conceived by his mind'.[6] We appreciate today the psychological complexity of the man and the effort of his striving as much as his genius.

The Codex Leicester is based on minute observations of nature in an attempt to understand natural phenomena. Leonardo claimed that 'nature is my only master'. With his respect for nature and his buoyant faith in the development of technical solutions to human problems, he stands as a precursor, the first 'modern' man.

The Boulton and Watt engine at the Powerhouse Museum. Leonardo da Vinci studied and analysed the components of machinery and understood the practical applications of technology. He designed devices that used various energy sources – human power, water power and even steam power. The complex machinery of the Industrial Revolution was still based on the fundamental mechanical principles that evolved from the innovations of Leonardo's time. Built in 1785, the Boulton and Watt engine is the oldest surviving rotative steam engine in the world. It was designed by James Watt and financed and manufactured by Matthew Boulton.

Photo: Powerhouse Museum

ENDNOTES

1. Baldassare Castiglione, *Il Cortegiano* [*The Courtier*], 1528, quoted in *Book of the Courtier*, Penguin, USA, 1976.

2. Giorgio Vasari, *Lives of the most eminent Italian architects, painters and sculptors*, tr Benedette Calzavara, Torino, 1957, p 546.

3. Leonardo da Vinci, Codex Atlanticus, Milan, Biblioteca Ambrosiana, folio 391r-a.

4. Codex Leicester, Sheet 14A, folio 14r, tr Carlo Pedretti.

5. James E Lovelock, *Gaia, a new look at life on Earth*, Oxford University Press, 1979.

6. Vasari, op cit, p 547.

THE STRUCTURE AND DATING OF THE CODEX LEICESTER

Carlo Pedretti

Each of the eighteen double sheets of the Codex Leicester measures approximately 296 x 438 mm. Each sheet was folded, so that a sheet is composed of two folios and each folio of two pages, also designated as recto and verso (abbreviated r and v). Each page usually consists of a main body of writing with long lines and a narrow space in the right margin for illustrations (often diagrammatic) and additional comments. The illustrations, which total about 360, are occasionally placed at the bottom and in a few instances also across the page. The sheets were bound together in the 17th century in a single signature. This was the result of piling up eighteen double sheets folded in the middle. The folios are numbered consecutively from 1 to 36 by a 16th-century hand.

Leonardo worked on one individual double sheet at a time, filling its four sides presumably in a backward sequence, so that if one were to designate the four sides in the pagination sequence 1 to 4, it could be said that Leonardo started on 4 and ended on 1. This 4-to-1 procedure can be ascertained on the basis of Leonardo's own references on a double sheet of geometric and canal studies of 1509, reconstructed with two sheets of the Codex Atlanticus, folios 82r-a and 179r-a. The same can be seen in many of his anatomical manuscripts of about 1508–10 in the Royal Library at Windsor Castle, as in the case of a double sheet with geometric studies dated 1509, Royal Library 12658 and 19145. The reconstructed double sheets of Anatomical Manuscript (MS) A of 1510 are again of the same kind. It is clear that Leonardo, regardless of the matter in hand, always tried to contain a set of observations within the space of a

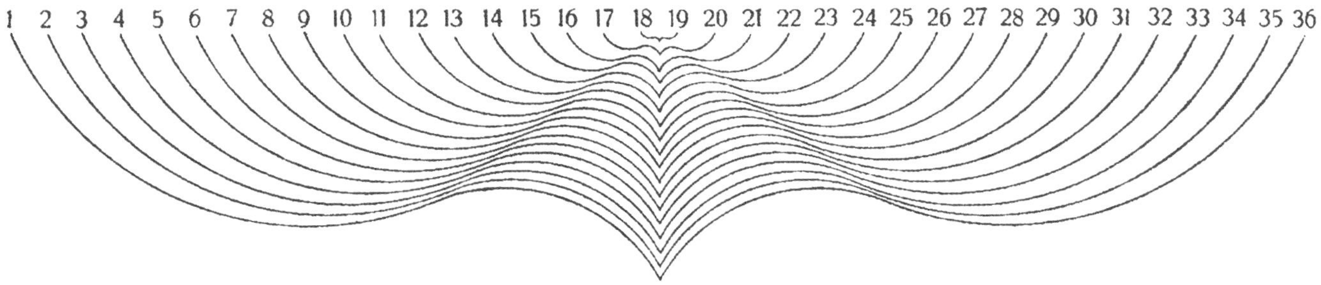

Diagram of the physical makeup of the Codex Leicester.

page and very seldom moved on to the next page with the same argument. Yet the pages of a double sheet always have something in common, being the record of a single impulse in Leonardo's thought. The same can be said of the style of drawing and the ductus (special characteristics) of the handwriting, as is clearly shown in the reconstruction of his anatomical manuscripts. A study of his papers in the order in which he compiled them can add greatly to our understanding of the development of his theories and views — a development that often consists of hesitations, reconsideration and second thoughts. With this also comes a better understanding of the development of the style of his drawings.

The Codex Leicester is now disbound to show how its pages faced one another when Leonardo compiled them. This has resulted in a 'pile' of eighteen double sheets, as shown in the diagram above. Leonardo himself kept an account of the number of 'cases' collected on each page, and from time to time he would add up these numbers. The Leonardo scholar Gerolamo Calvi has taken this as a reflection of the sequence of compilation of the double sheets, from the middle to the outer ones. However, the simple process of piling up sheets suggests the reverse process, that is that the first sheets — conjugate folios 1 and 36, 2 and 35, and so on — were placed flat at the bottom and the later ones piled on top of them to become the central part of the codex. Textual analysis led Calvi to the conclusion that the whole codex was compiled 'not before 1503–4' but 'presumably about 1506–8', the pages at the beginning and at the end being those closer to 1508. Ductus and style might justify the suspicion that at least part of the compilation could be closer to 1510. Apparently, Kenneth Clark had already thought of such a later date when he dated a number of Leonardo drawings at Windsor circa 1508–10 by reference to the Codex Leicester.

Ultimately the dating of the Codex Leicester has been set at 1508–10 by this evidence and by comparison with other Leonardo manuscripts. A full discussion appears in my introduction to the Codex Hammer [Leicester], published in 1994 by Christie's for the auction of the codex, and in the notes to my translation of the codex (Florence, Giunti Barbèra, 1987). It is summarised here.

Memoranda written by Leonardo in the Codex Atlanticus, which can be dated with reasonable accuracy to about 1507–8, as well as scientific and autobiographical notes in that codex, suggest a date close to 1508–10 for the whole of the Codex Leicester, or at least for part of the compilation. The Codex Leicester was probably begun in Florence at about the same time as the Arundel MS, which is dated 22 March 1508 on the first sheet. Hence the immediacy of the references to Florence and Tuscany in Leonardo's discussions on physical geography, as Calvi has pointed out. It is even reasonable to assume, as Calvi does, that the initial phase of the compilation was carried out in Vinci, near Florence, where Leonardo seems to have had access to facilities for water experiments, as implied by remarks such as those found in the marginal notes on folio 9v: 'Test at your pit what is the course taken by the object *n*...'

More tangible evidence of Leonardo's presence in the Vinci area in 1504 or on some later occasion is provided by two drawings in the Royal Library at Windsor, 12675 and 12676, which originally formed a single sheet the size of one double sheet of the Codex Leicester; in fact, the paper is of the same stock, showing the same tulip watermark as three sheets of the Codex Leicester (folios 6, 7, and 8). The double sheet at Windsor shows, among other plans, Leonardo's plan for an artificial lake at Vinci.

Finally, it can be shown that the compilation of the Codex Leicester was continued in Milan at the same time as that of Paris Manuscript F, a notebook that was begun in Milan on 12 September 1508, and that in style, ductus and content is related to the material in the Codex Atlanticus, in which the memoranda noted above are written. The sections on the moon on folios 1 and 2 of the Codex Leicester and those on cosmology on the conjugate folios 35 and 36 are paralleled by texts in the first thirty sheets of the Arundel MS, which dates from about 1508. Even the celebrated reference to submarine warfare on folio 22v can be related to the 1508 section of the Arundel MS, which in fact contains studies of a diving apparatus. And the study of the meeting and compenetration of circular waves on folio 23r (and on the facing and conjugate folio 14v) is related to diagrams and notes in the Codex Atlanticus, folio 83v-b, the parent sheet of the Windsor fragment, Royal Library 12353, that contains a study for the Trivulzio Monument.

The monumental contribution of Calvi, who first published the Codex Leicester in facsimile, provides the foundation for whatever approach may be chosen in the study of this extensive and complex document of Leonardo's thought. The main objective, however, should remain that of establishing a chronological focus for it, so that its intimate relationship with Leonardo's production as a painter can be better understood. In fact, the cosmological views expressed in the Codex Leicester are given visual shape in Leonardo's paintings, from the *Madonna of the Yarn-winder* and the Louvre *St Anne* to the *Mona Lisa*, as recent scholarship has eloquently shown. (See in particular K D Keele's 'The Genesis of Mona Lisa' in *Journal of the History of Medicine and Allied Sciences,* xiv, 1959; K Clark's 'Mona Lisa' in *Burlington Magazine* cxv, 1973; and M Kemp's *Leonardo da Vinci: the marvellous works of nature and man*, London, 1981, chapters iv and v, and 'Analogy and Observation in the Codex Hammer' in *Studi vinciani in memoria di Nando de Toni*, Brescia, 1986. See also C Pedretti's edition of Leonardo's *Landscapes, plants and water studies*, Windsor, 1982.)

About one-third of the illustrations in the Codex Leicester is made up of fascinating representations of water currents, leaps, and vortexes. These are conceptually and stylistically related to a vast body of observations in all fields of natural science as found in other Leonardo manuscripts and drawings dating from the time of the Codex Leicester and later, that is, the last ten years of Leonardo's life. All forms of organic life and every aspect of growth and transformation in nature, from plants to animals and from combustion to decay, come to be associated by analogical process to the dynamics of water. This is made visually eloquent by the splendid series of water studies at Windsor, including the so-called 'Deluge series'.

It is not surprising, therefore, that on one of those Windsor drawings Leonardo should call attention to the fact that the movement of water is comparable to that of human hair: 'Observe the motion of the surface of water how it resembles that of hair, which has two motions, of which one depends on the weight of the hair, the other on the direction of the curls; thus the water forms eddying whirlpools, one part of which is due to the impetus of the principal current and the other to the incidental motion and return flow.'

THE PAGES OF THE CODEX LEICESTER

with texts by Carlo Pedretti

The numbering of the sheets and folios in this publication follows the system used by Carlo Pedretti in the facsimile edition of the codex published with his translation into English in 1987. Each of the eighteen double sheets of the codex is labelled A and B, indicating the front and back, and is then divided into two folios. Each folio is made up of a recto and a verso page.

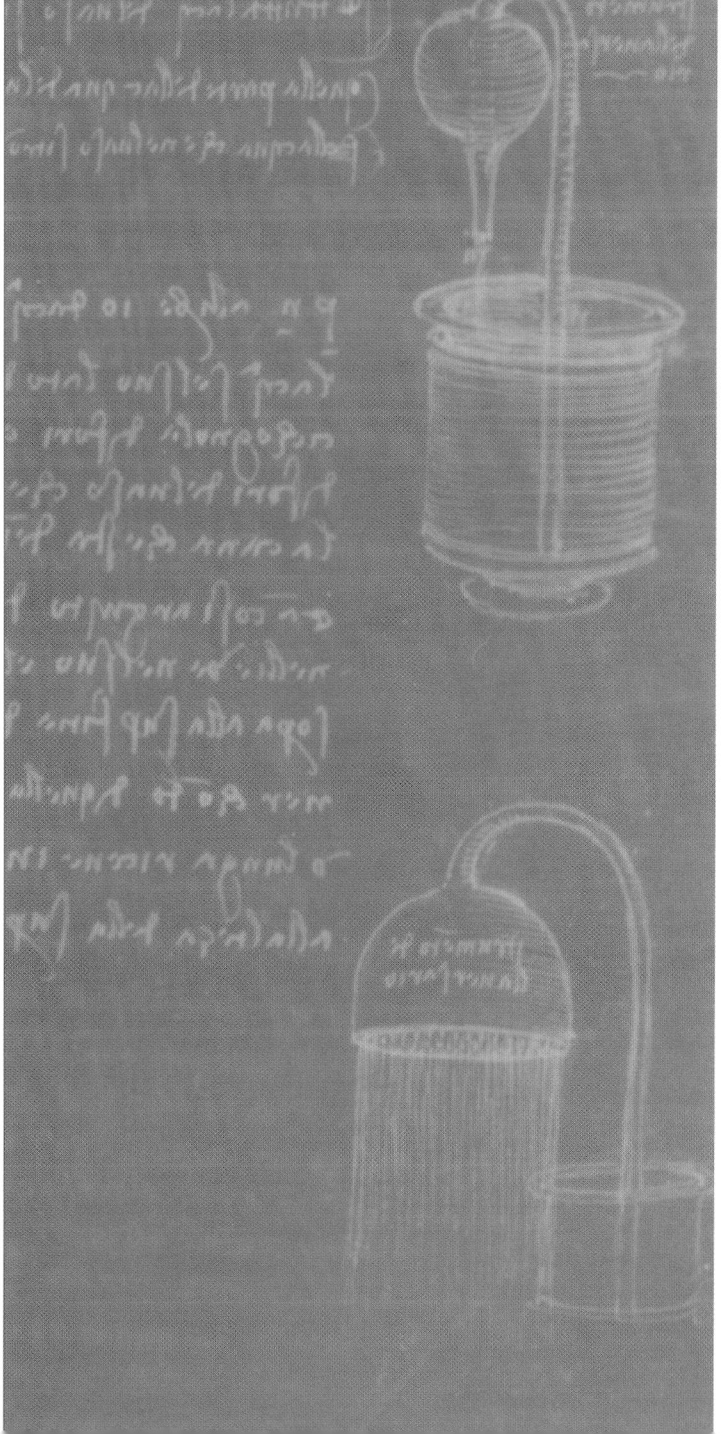

Sheet 1A, folio 36v

In Leonardo's time, there were thought to be four building blocks of nature: earth, water, air and fire. These four cosmic elements were arranged in concentric spheres according to their relative densities, with earth, the heaviest, at the centre. Next came water, then air, and finally, in the upper atmosphere, fire.

These beliefs were predicated on centuries of scientific thinking about the universe. Scientists, including Leonardo, accepted Ptolemy's revision of Aristotle's scheme of a universe composed of fifty-five concentric spheres. According to Aristotle, each planet inhabited its own sphere, which was concentric with the earth at the centre of the world — the cosmos itself was spherical in shape.

In his second-century treatise *Hypotheses on the Planets*, Ptolemy proposed that the planets revolve in eccentric orbits within these concentric spheres, thus allowing for the possibility that each planet has its own centre of gravity, surrounded by its own concentric spheres of water, air and fire.

From these theories, Leonardo assumes the same may be true of the earth's moon, and thus writes of its watery surface. The persona of his famed 'adversary' argues that any water on the moon would naturally fall to the earth by the action of gravity. Leonardo retorts that if the moon's water fell, then the moon itself would fall, and says, 'Therefore, not falling, it is a clear proof that the water up there and earth are sustained with their other elements, just as the heavy and light elements down here sustain themselves in a space that is lighter than themselves.' In effect, he concludes that the moon has its own gravity.

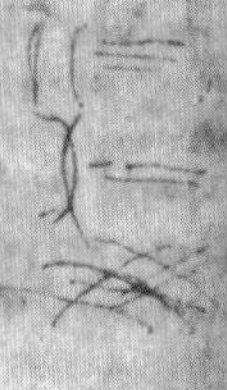

Sheet 1A, folio 1r

The illustrations make this page one of the most famous of the Codex Leicester. They explore the geometry and astronomy of the relationships of the sun, earth and moon, a central topic in the medieval science of cosmology. Consider the large vertical figure of the sun shining on the earth. Leonardo writes at length about how the position of the viewer, on the earth or above it, determines how much of the sun he sees. 'Here an effect contrary to the law of perspective takes place, in that those who are farther from the solar body see less of it; and they are those who are towards the two poles, namely *f m*, who see of the sun no more than the part *a n* or the part *m r*.'

Leonardo works here to explain why the light of the moon is less bright than the light of the sun, and why the moon reflects an uneven brightness — a question dating from antiquity.

By the fifteenth century, everyone agreed that the moon was illuminated primarily by reflected sunlight. Leonardo speculates on the moon's composition, knowing only that the planet appears shiny and reflective when seen from the earth. The problem was to learn whether a smooth, perfectly round sphere was responsible for the specific kind of light the moon displays.

Leonardo presents two explanations. The moon, like the other planets, is transparent and crystalline, but to a lesser degree because it is closer to the earth. Since sunlight does not fully penetrate the moon, some of it reflects to the earth. Or, he asks, could the moon be composed of different densities, as the earth was believed to be?

Leonardo argues here and on six other pages that the outer sphere of the moon is liquid, with standing waves that reflect some, but not all, of the sun's light. Lustre, of itself, does not sufficiently explain the luminescence of the moon. If this hypothesis is true, then 'the light will be given to each wave individually and then to all as a whole, causing a great deal of brightness'. The light breaks into many images from the choppy water, accounting for its lack of uniform brightness.

Leonardo continues to treat his scientific explorations like a scholastic argument. He makes alternative propositions, then roundly disputes them with his invented adversaries. He concludes, in this instance, with a geometric demonstration of the action of light in straight lines, which proves his hypothesis.

At the bottom of the page, the scallop-edged sphere represents the waves on the surface of the moon. Leonardo shows that rays of light striking and rebounding from this surface do not intermingle and become confused (as claimed by an 'adversary' on folio 1v).

This same point-to-point analysis of the action of light is the basis for Leonardo's defence of painting as a science of optics concerned with the graphic representation of appearances on a flat surface.

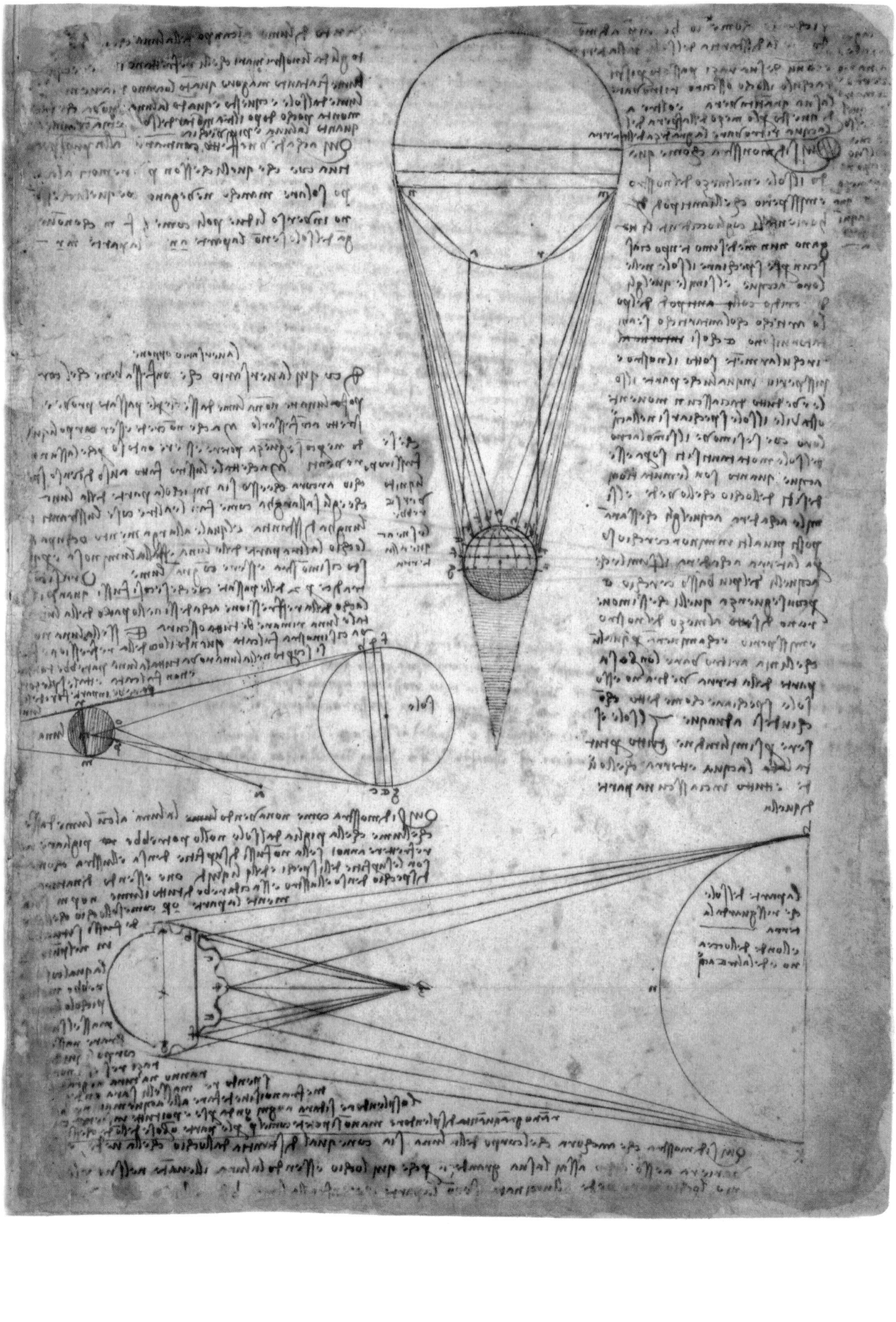

Sheet 1B, folio 1v

This page discusses the earth as a living body, the underlying theme of Leonardo's treatise on water. He presents two major subjects: the motion of water on the earth and the possibility of water on the moon. The upper part of the page details European and Middle Eastern geographical and geological history based on the pattern of rivers and the effects of their flow over thousands of years. Leonardo considers how the eroding action of rivers is responsible for lakes in valleys as well as seashells in the mountains.

The main questions Leonardo addresses throughout the codex concern the circulation of water in the body of the earth. Here he asks two questions: How do rivers reach the tops of mountains, given that water moves on its own only when it descends? Does the great Deluge adequately account for the presence of seashells and aquatic fossils on mountaintops?

Leonardo approaches the first question by applying Aristotelian theories of movement and the second by challenging the traditional biblical account.

The lower part of the page discusses the cause of the moon's uneven brightness. Leonardo maintains that unlike a smooth, mirrored surface, the moon's water-covered surface is textured and three-dimensional. Therefore, some of the light reflected from the sun is lost in shadows, which explains the pale brilliance of the moon's glow. The illustrations at midpage and below depict the sun's rays striking the moon and reflecting back to the human eye.

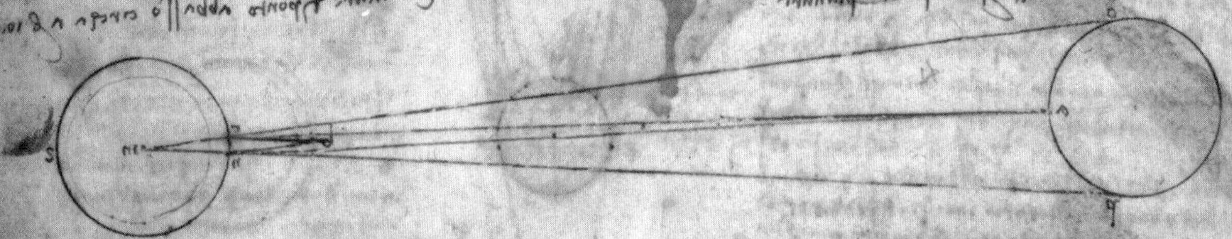

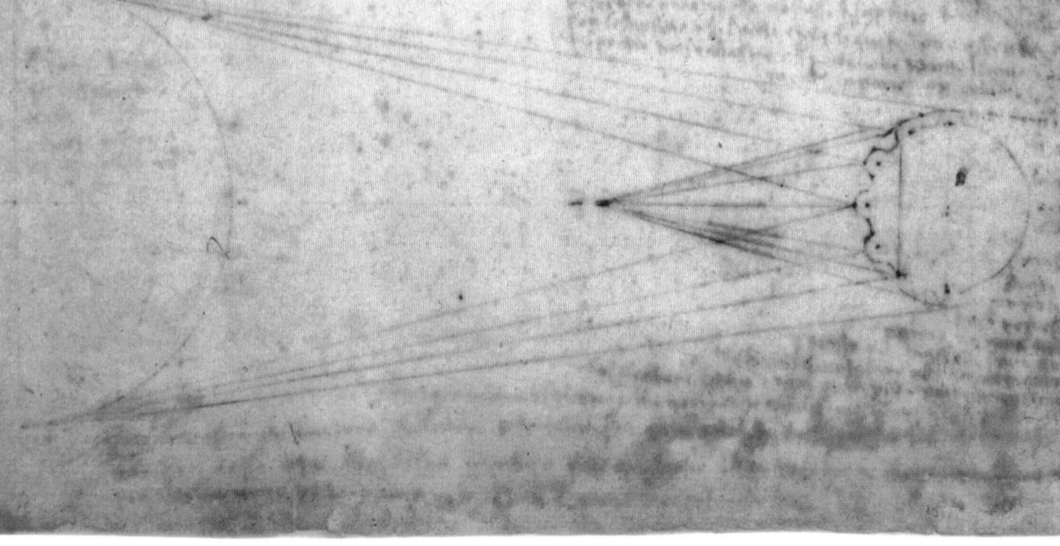

Sheet 1B, folio 36r

'Of the earth itself' is Leonardo's title for this discussion about the body of the earth and how land masses project from the sphere of water. His sketches illustrate the concept on which he bases this global theory: the earth is a cavern filled with water, which rises to the surface through a system of subterranean veins. From this idea comes his hypothesis on the origin of mountains.

With his friend the mathematician Luca Pacioli, Leonardo developed a system in which the cosmic elements correspond to the shapes of geometric bodies: cube for earth, icosahedron for water, octahedron for air and pyramid for fire. But did Leonardo accept this Platonic view literally? To approach this question, one must refer to his adherence to the traditional theories of the macrocosm, defined as the four concentric spheres of the four cosmic elements: fire, the outermost, then air, water and earth as the hidden core.

Taking the simple Platonic scheme as his starting point, Leonardo explains how earth is removed from the core by earthquakes and similar phenomena to create a marbled mass. He then returns to the theme of subterranean waters that erode the earth's interior, causing caverns to collapse. As these caverns crumble, water fills them, which explains why the seas remain at a constant level and why the earth remains in balance. This idea, familiar to him from Ristoro d'Arezzo, is the most innovative visual model of the dynamic balance of the world in the entire codex. Cross-sectional diagrams indicate how the layers of earth and water continually fold in upon themselves, pulled towards the centre by gravity, pushed towards the periphery by the lightening of their mass.

The page ends with a reference to fossilised saltwater shells, many of which Leonardo found at different elevations on his paleontological expeditions in Lombardy. He reasons that since the earth has fallen in on itself and the oceans have filled in the spaces, 'marine shells and oysters ... are seen in high mountains'. With evidence that seemingly verifies his water and mountain theories, he concludes that 'these are found in all the valleys that open out into the seas'.

In the final synthesis, Leonardo combined the analyses performed under two separate categories, the universal and the particular.

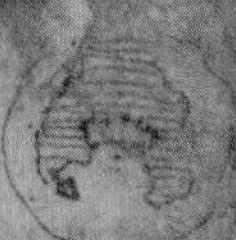

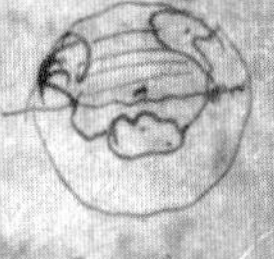

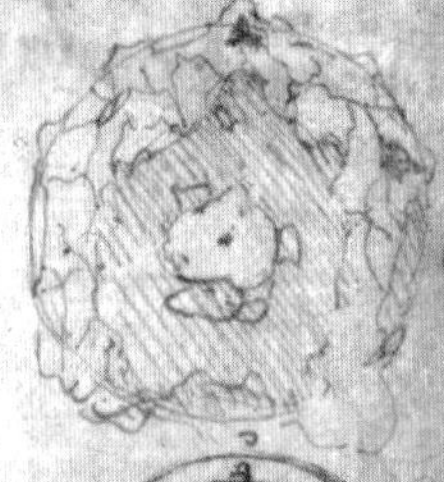

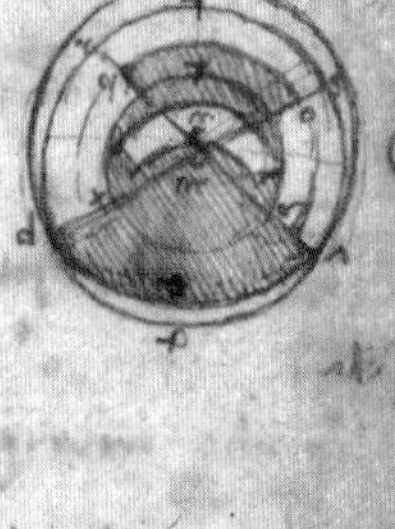

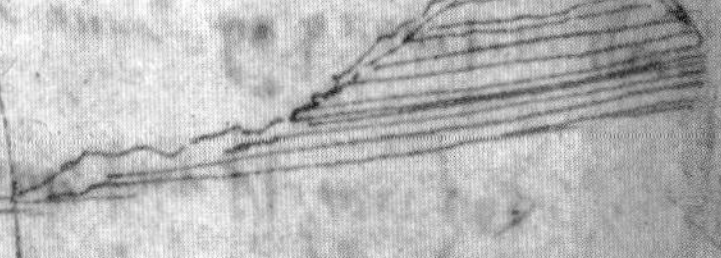

Sheet 2A, folio 35v

This page begins with a question: Does earth or water cover more of the planet? Leonardo postulates an equal amount of each. The simple diagram of a triangle inscribed in a circle demonstrates the balance of actual materials that make up the planet. This balance allows Leonardo to speculate further on how the gravity of the planet is also maintained in dynamic balance.

Leonardo considers gravity in terms very different from ours. The problem of gravity that most concerns him is recorded in a sequence of thoughts that bring us into intimate contact with the workings of his mind. How, he asks, can we account for the centre of gravity, given that rock strata of various densities and even water of varying densities are intermingled on the planet?

Leonardo distinguishes three kinds of gravity, or centres, using categories developed by medieval scholastic writers. The simplest kind does not concern him for long because it is unproblematic: the geometric centre of the planet. This is the 'centre of magnitude', which he defines as being 'separated equally from the opposite extremities of the body that encloses it, whether it be uniform or not'. Like a 'ball of any material', this kind of gravity is defined only by its location at the geometric centre of the world.

The second kind is natural gravity. If the 'machine of the earth' were perfectly spherical and contained equal amounts of water and earthen material, the centre of natural gravity would coincide with the geometric centre. (This kind of gravity, in modern science, corresponds to a body's centre of mass.) If the land projects in equal amounts on opposite sides, or the earth is entirely surrounded by water on the outside, the fluid will fill the interstices and form a smooth outer surface owing to gravitational force. The centres of gravity will be at the same location under these conditions. In Leonardo's terms, natural gravity is concentric with the geometric centre. (We would say that they coincide.) In this case, Leonardo quips, the centres would certainly coincide, 'but there would be no land animals'.

Accidental gravity is more difficult to define. For Nicole Oresme, one of Leonardo's most sophisticated medieval sources, the denser the material, the heavier it is, and gravity attracts the heaviest materials to the centre of the world. In Leonardo's usage, accidental gravity pertains to an object in motion — for instance, when a spinning top maintains its equilibrium, the centre of its accidental gravity is the central axis. The same principle can be applied to any irregularly shaped object: when the object is spinning in equilibrium, its accidental gravity is centred. By the same token, an object at rest has no accidental gravity.

In the final analysis, Leonardo's ideas about the body of the earth were the product of tradition, but they had no precedent.

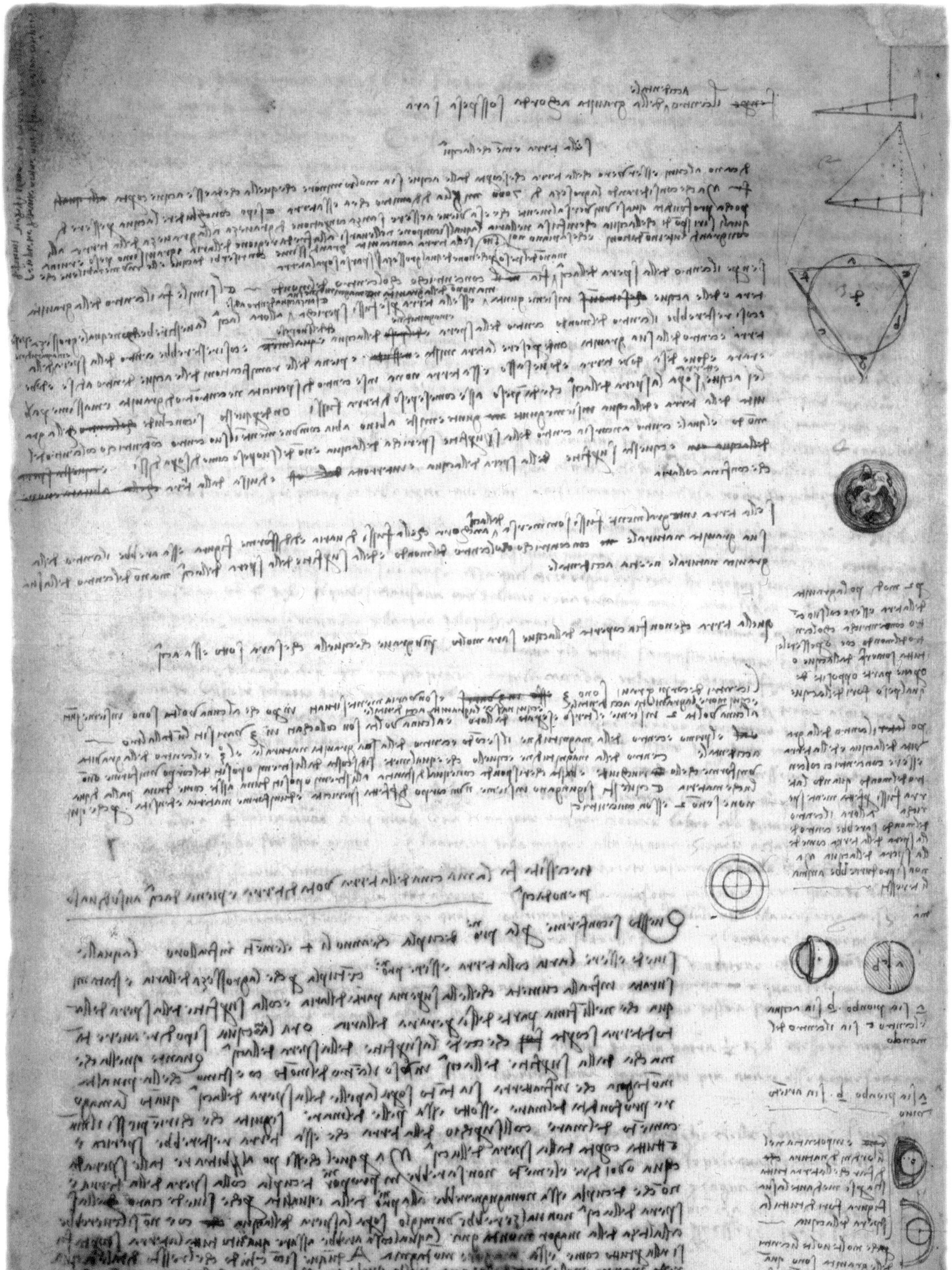

Sheet 2A, folio 2r

This page is titled 'Of the moon. No solid body is lighter than air.' The notes are clear and orderly, the diagrams are accurate, and the crescent moon at the bottom of the page has a captivating presence.

By the fifteenth century, Ptolemy's 'eccentric orbit' theory — that the moon and other celestial bodies orbit the earth — was widely accepted. Leonardo's discussion of the moon and its own elements alludes to Ptolemy's revision of Aristotle's view that all celestial bodies circled the unmoving earth, each at a different level and each in its own sphere concentric with the earth at the centre of the world.

Leonardo believed that the moon has an atmosphere and a nature similar to those of the earth and, therefore, the same physical laws. The diagram crossing the middle of the page helps to show that the moon's surface has substance and weight.

The question that concerns Leonardo is whether the moon is heavy enough to keep the watery sphere at its surface from falling away to the earth. That the water does not fall 'is a clear sign that the moon is clothed with its own elements, namely water, air and fire, and so sustains itself in that part of space as does our earth with its elements in this other part of space; and that the heavy bodies perform the same function in its elements as the other heavy bodies do in ours'.

Leonardo clearly restates the arguments made on folios 1r and 1v: if the moon were without waves, its radiance would be almost equal to that of the sun. 'Some have believed that the moon has in part a light of its own in addition to that which is given it by the sun, and that this light is due to the cause already mentioned, namely that our seas are illuminated by the sun.'

Leonardo means that the dim glow of the rest of the moon during the crescent phase is due to light reflected from the earth's oceans back to the moon's darkened portion. He adds that this light is difficult to see owing to the mutual enhancement of light and dark when they are juxtaposed. The principle of bright contrast derives from his study of optics. To better see this pale light in the moon's crescent phase, Leonardo recommends covering up the bright part with one's hand.

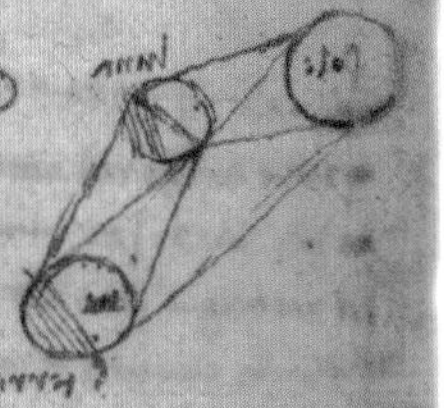

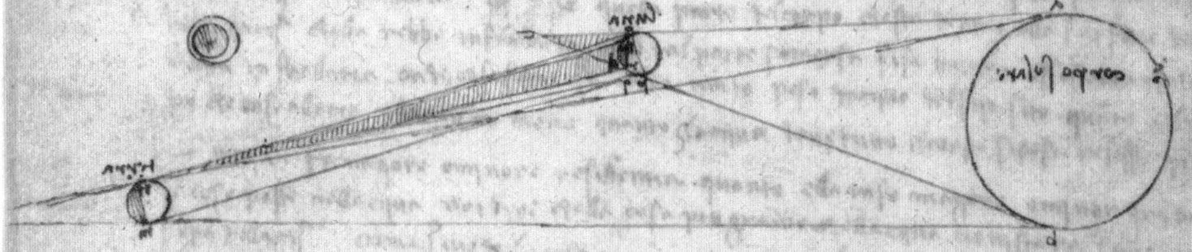

Sheet 2B, folio 2v

'How to empty a swamp that flows into the sea' presents Leonardo's plan for clearing a swamp — a problem he was frequently called on to solve.

In the second paragraph, Leonardo argues that if the moon did not have its own centre of gravity, its watery sphere would fall to earth. This argument owes its origins to Archimedes' treatise on floating bodies. Fragments of this discourse are preserved in Leonardo's notes in the Codex Atlanticus.

Leonardo next considers the role of light reflected from the earth's seas onto the moon's surface as viewed from various positions during the day and night. His original considerations are reminiscent of studies of the changing position of the sun that he conducted in about 1505.

An interesting aspect of this study lies in the glimpse it offers of Leonardo's method. He begins with somewhat banal observations, tests hypotheses easily, and treats each step forward as a means to continue, rather than as an end in itself. 'I will not consider the demonstrations here, because I will reserve them for the ordered work; my concern now is to find cases and inventions, gathering them as they occur to me; then I shall have them in order, placing those of the same kind together; therefore you will not wonder nor will you laugh at me, reader, if here I make such great jumps from one subject to the other.' Leonardo seems to allow his thoughts to proceed and expand, constantly ranging from the particular to the universal and then back again.

come si debbe votare uno stagno che sbocchi nel mare.

[illegible]

[illegible]

N[illegible]

[illegible]

Sheet 2B, folio 35r

Leonardo here considers tides and opposing water currents to advance his studies on the movement of water. The tides in Flanders, he warrants, are due not to the moon but to the volume of river water that enters the Mediterranean: 'Near to Flanders, the sea rises and falls about 20 braccia every six hours and this as is clearly seen is not caused by the moon. This variation in the rising and falling may occur through the swelling up of the waters which are poured into the Mediterranean Sea by the rivers from Africa, Asia and Europe.'

His scrutiny of minute water confluences in small canals gives him cause to think about the circulation of water on a global scale: 'I have seen in the case of two small canals, each 2 braccia wide, how their waters clashed together with unequal force, and then united ... they formed there a flow and ebb.'

The page concludes with an observation on the formation of smooth and stratified rocks created by the settling of silt in the sea. Leonardo shares again his method of organisation — he is gathering cases and demonstrations 'as they occur to me'.

Sheet 3A, folio 34v

With a dozen sketches of vessels and siphon systems, this page gives the impression that Leonardo worked in his laboratory conducting imaginative experiments.

In the main text, Leonardo contrasts two ways of calculating the location of the centre of the earth. In this context, he distinguishes between the 'universal watery sphere' and the particular watery sphere. The Aristotelian distinction between the universal and the particular is one of the most important principles governing the conceptual organisation of the entire codex. Generally speaking, the universal concerns that which endures for ever, unchanging, like geometry — for instance, the underlying form of a perfectly round sphere is universal. The particular concerns the individual, physical manifestation of form in matter.

Leonardo names two conditions that pertain to the universal watery sphere: all universal waters are without movement, and the boundaries of their surfaces are equidistant from the centre of the world. His examples of universal 'centres of the sphericity' include canals, ditches, ponds, fountains, wells, stagnant rivers, lakes, marshes, swamps and seas.

As for particular watery spheres, he writes, 'The centre of a particular sphere of water is that which occurs in the tiniest particles of dew, which are seen in perfect roundness clustering upon the leaves of the plants on which it falls; it is of such lightness that it does not flatten itself upon the spot on which it rests, and it is almost supported by the atmosphere that surrounds it, so that it does not itself exert any pressure or form any foundation.'

To explain the location of the centre of a drop of water, Leonardo describes, with characteristic precision, the action of a dewdrop as it grows in size and changes shape. Its spherical shape flattens, owing to increasing internal pressure on its surface tension. Text and illustrations together explain that as the dome of the drop flattens out under these conditions, its surface comes closer to the perfectly round shape of the universal sphere. This argument has its root in the belief that geometric form is a defining force of nature. The governing factor is the attraction of the curve of the dewdrop to the curve of the universal sphere of water. With this force, mass overcomes surface tension.

Leonardo directs this argument against, among others, Pliny the Elder's belief that the height of the seas was higher than that of the mountains, which is key to the entire theory of the circulation of water in the body of the earth.

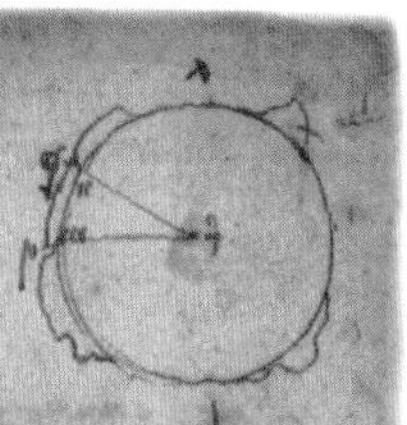

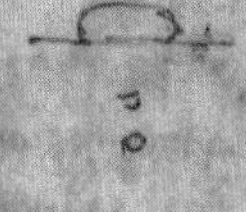

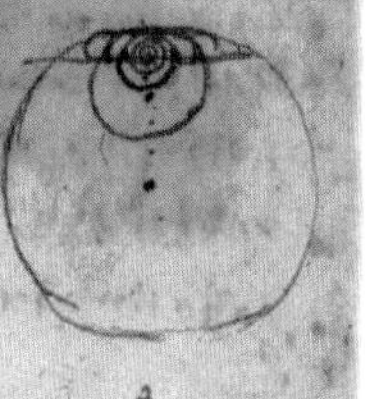

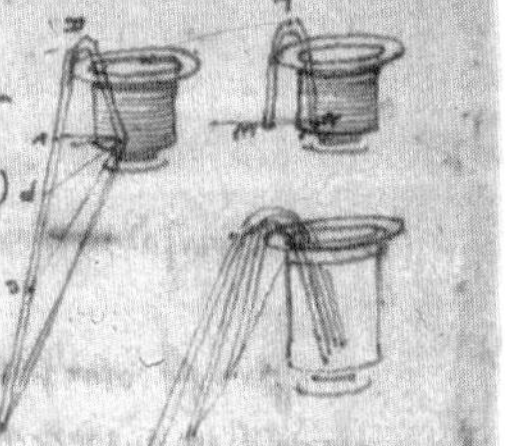

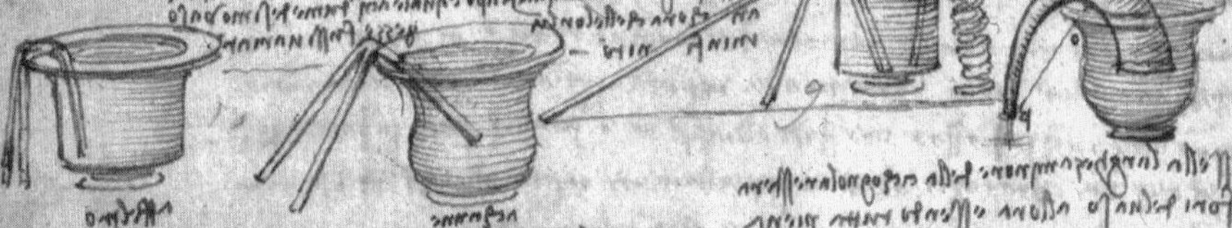

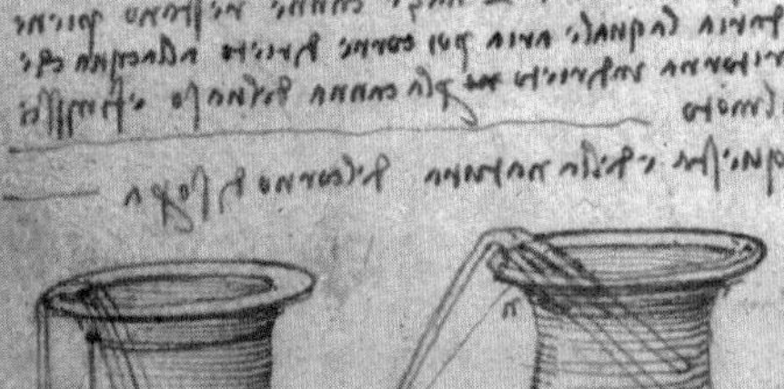

Sheet 3A, folio 3r

Here Leonardo questions traditional theories of how water originates in mountain caverns. He cites cases contrary to the assumption on which the traditional theory depends — that caverns remain constantly full. This leads him to consider specific causes of water erosion.

Leonardo challenges Ristoro d'Arezzo's 1282 treatise, *La composizione del mondo*, specifically its theory on continuous circulation of water throughout the body of the earth. The main problem is to account for the presence of water at the summits of mountains. Ancient writers, such as Pliny the Elder and Seneca, assumed that the highest oceans were higher than the summits of the highest mountains. This assumption, based on a faulty geometric model of the earth, was not questioned by Ristoro. Whereas Ristoro believed that water rose to the mountaintops primarily by siphoning through porous earth, Leonardo considers the various densities of soil and the ability of water to penetrate them; why no more water flows in the summer, after the snows have melted, than in winter; and the actual composition of the earth in terms of layers of rock and soil.

Throughout the codex, Leonardo's probing discussions on water-filled caverns show that his understanding of the geography of the earth increased through writing, reading, and direct observation. As his understanding grew, so did his artistic and scientific worldview.

Sheet 3B, folio 3v

This page is probably the last Leonardo wrote about the circulation of water in the body of the earth. He considers two explanations for water rising to the summits of mountains: water could be absorbed upwards as into a porous sponge; or, within the caverns of the earth, water could evaporate from the sun's heat and form vapour, much as the sun's heat generates clouds above the earth. Using prevailing climatic conditions and differences in temperatures to reason this second argument, he eventually rejects it. In so doing, he is led to the analogy of the process of distillation, a connection made by Ristoro d'Arezzo. Leonardo also theorises that heat generated from the centre of the earth would affect the levels of the oceans. He imagines a glass model of the earth as a still to explain how the condensation of water is a 'downward process'.

Leonardo poses a puzzle in his description of distillation. The diagrams of inverted glass flasks and the accompanying text describe what happens when a burning coal is placed inside a vessel inverted over water. In the ancient version of this experiment, described by Heron of Alexandria, combustion consumes the air inside the vessel, and the water level rises. However, Leonardo places the burning coal 'on top of the vessel' rather than within, and he draws the diagram accordingly. Despite this deviation, he accurately describes that a vacuum effect, not heat, draws the water up.

He applies the specific result of the experiment to the real world, arguing that in an open system — with the necessary hole on the side of the mountain as an outlet for water — the application of heat from above would not draw water up but air in. 'And if you want to convince yourself that water is not drawn up by fire, make a hole in the vessel *m* at point *p*, and you will see that the water will not leave its place.'

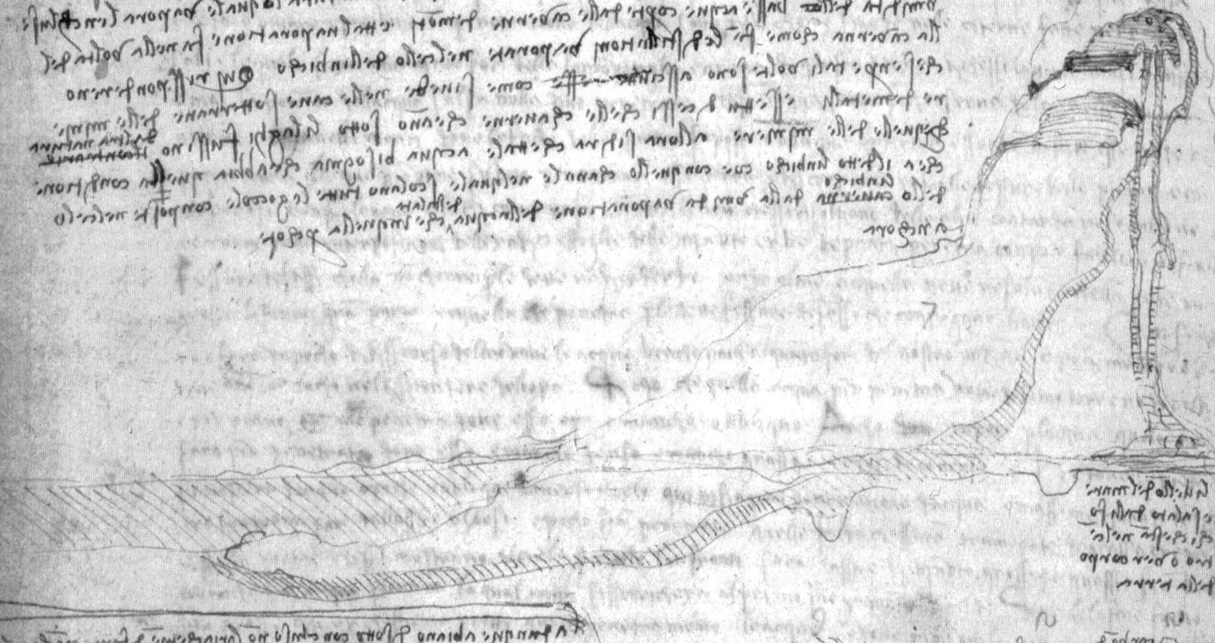

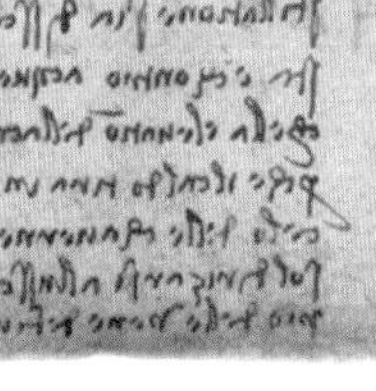

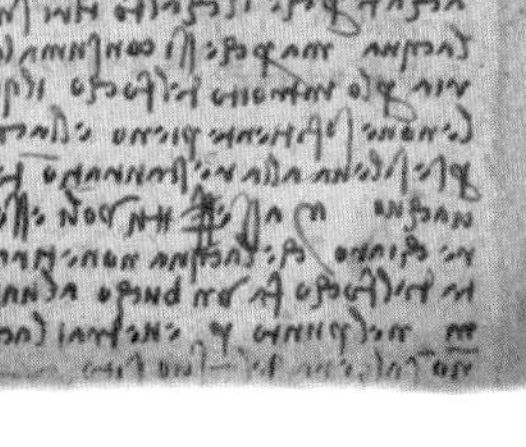

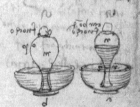

Sheet 3B, folio 34r

On this page, Leonardo offers a poetic and quite personal observation, likening human existence to the vital life of our planet earth. 'Nothing grows in a spot where there is neither sentient, vegetal nor rational life ... We may say that the earth has a spirit of growth, and that its flesh is the soil; its bones are the successive strata of the rocks; ... its cartilage is the tufa stone; its blood the veins of its waters. The lake of the blood that lies around the heart is the ocean. Its breathing is by the increase and decrease of the blood in its pulses, and even so in the earth is the ebb and flow of the sea.'

He also offers an observation about the circulation of water with an accompanying geometric diagram that relates to Ristoro d'Arezzo's conception of the composition of the earth, describing the relationship of the land to the sea on the basis of the sphere's geometry.

In Leonardo's illustration, the circumference of the semicircle represents half the surface of the earth. A line is drawn to connect the two endpoints to create a curved segment. The endpoints represent two points of land, and the part of the circumference between them represents the sea. Ristoro argues that the sea is 'higher than' the land because it bulges 'above' the land. Leonardo questions this geometric model with an analogy of a bowl of water and concludes that anything that projects above the surface, such as a mountain, is higher than any sea.

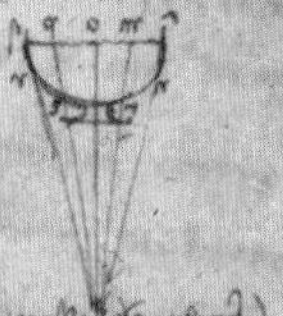

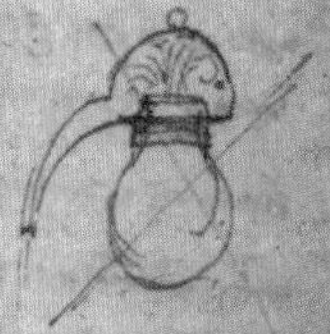

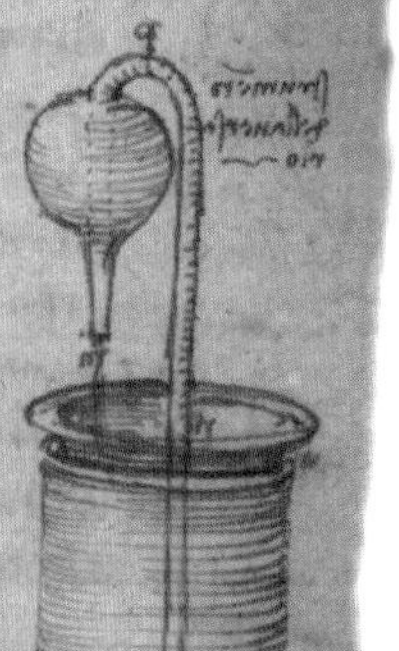

Sheet 4A, folio 33v

A twelve-line passage compares the body of the earth to the body of an animal. This analogy of macrocosm to microcosm originated in ancient philosophical writings, but Leonardo develops his thoughts in a strictly scientific direction.

He devotes most of this page to the earth's rivers. As elsewhere in the Codex Leicester, his descriptions suggest both visual and literary sources for his thinking. 'The body of the earth, like the bodies of animals, is interwoven with a network of veins which are all joined together and are formed for the nutrition and vivification of the earth and of its creatures; and they originate in the depths of the sea, and there after many revolutions they have to return through the rivers formed by the high burstings of these veins.'

Jean-Paul Richter, in 1883, and other scholars proposed that Leonardo had travelled to the East and elsewhere. This assumption was based on texts like this one and Leonardo's famous letters from the East. We now know that Leonardo's worldly attitude was developed through armchair travelling, inspired in part by the availability of books through the new printing technology.

Delle diminutioni de fiumi

Il corpo della terra a similitudine de corpi delli animali [illegible]

[illegible]

Sheet 4A, folio 4r

This discussion of atmospheric colour applies equally to Leonardo's scientific and artistic activities. 'I say that the blue which is seen in the atmosphere is not its own colour but is caused by the heated moisture having evaporated into the most minute, imperceptible particles, which the beams of the solar rays attract and cause to seem luminous against the deep, intense darkness of the region of fire that forms a covering above them. And this may be seen, as I myself saw it, by anyone who ascends Mon Boso, a peak of the Alps that divide France from Italy, at the base of which spring the four rivers which flow as many different ways and irrigate all Europe, and there is no other mountain the base of which is at so great an elevation.'

In this belief, Leonardo follows Ristoro d'Arezzo's *La composizione del mondo*. In Leonardo's Aristotelian universe, air, the third element, surrounds the watery sphere of the earth, not far below the spheres of the sun and the moon.

Leonardo's passages on atmosphere suggest his intent to arrange his future treatise on water in the descending order of the elements.

Del colore dell'aria

Dico l'azzurro in che si mostra l'aria non essere suo proprio colore…

[illegible]

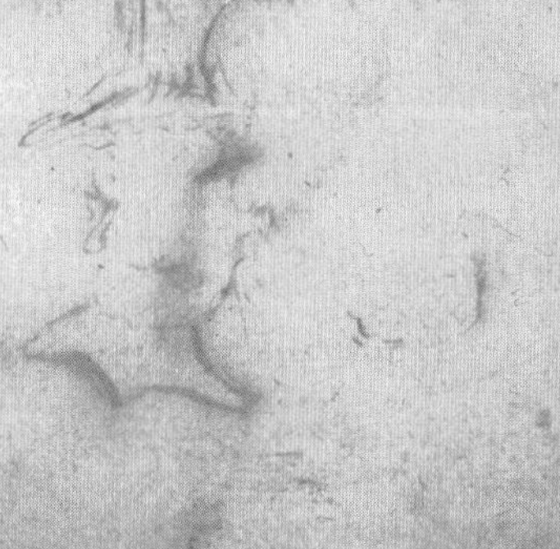

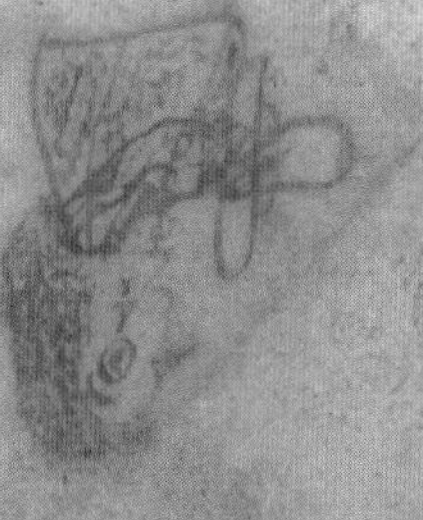

Sheet 4B, folio 4v

On this page, Leonardo addresses the fluid dynamics of water with the idea of measuring its velocity in quantitative terms. His descriptions of waves breaking and bouncing back take into account the complexity of their compound motion in both visual and geometric terms. We can follow his geometric analysis of the action of rebounding waves as a three-dimensional curling motion; as a wave descends from a higher point, it converges towards the centre of a lunar curvature:

'A wave does not bend or break on the side of its ordinary descent because the water runs away and finds no obstacle, but in its rise, from which it will fall, comes back and percusses the antecedent wave, which comes jousting with it, and above that it breaks without harming the one which it percusses.

'It is the falling wave which breaks, and not the one which receives it, because a percussed wave has greater and swifter motion than a striking one — and although the first percussion may cause to break somewhat the surface of the receiving water, the second leaps, being of less power, are not damaging and do not penetrate the water on which they fall.'

According to engineer Carlo Zammattio, Leonardo correctly guessed the law of wave motion — that each point struck by a wave becomes the origin of a new disturbance, all of which in concert determines the shape of an advancing wave front — a scientific investigation formulated by Christian Huygens in 1673.

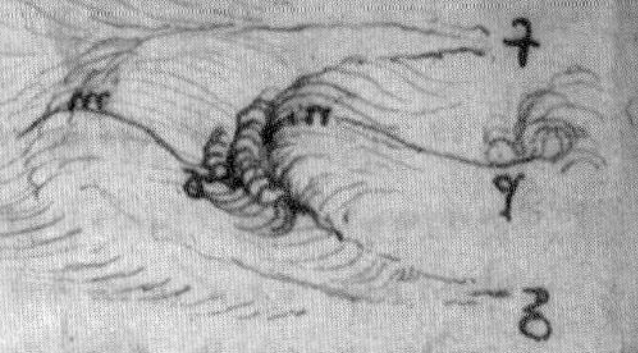

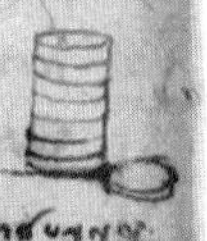

Sheet 4B, folio 33r

Leonardo addresses the flow of water through riverbeds and its consequences. He begins with the following thesis: 'The variety of the locations and velocity rates of the waters within their rivers is caused by the variety of bottom obliquities. The variety of the bottom obliquities of rivers is caused by the variety of swiftness of the water current.'

'The bottom of rivers is varied by the matter that the water course deposits there; and the variety in the water courses is brought about by their regularities in the riverbed. A drop of water that falls on a level place of even density will splash in such a way that the edges of its mark will be at an equal distance from its circumference; and so it does the contrary when it does not fall onto a level place.'

His sketch of a water drop hitting a flat surface exactly duplicates, but precedes by more than four and a half centuries, Harold Edgerton's classic photograph of an exploding, crown-like drop of milk.

[illegible]

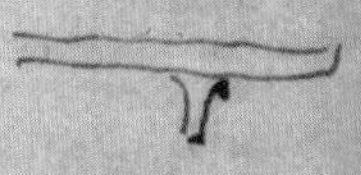

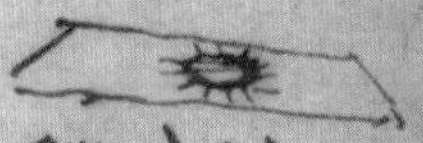

Sheet 5A, folio 32v

Leonardo again brings his expertise to bear on the problem of the body of the earth. He discusses the changing centre of the earth's gravity, which is caused by the planet's uneven density. This analysis was largely based on Jean Buridan's question of 'whether the world is always at rest at the centre of the universe', as Aristotle had maintained. Leonardo's thinking developed in a unique direction, and he concluded that the natural processes of the elevation and depression of land were analogous to the geometric transformation of one shape into another of equal volume. This topic occupied him for many years.

Related objections to traditional theories of the composition of the earth occur in the codex: on folio 10r, the changing centre of the earth's gravity owing to erosion; on folio 3v, the effect of the sun's heat on the inner structure of mountains and the theory that water is drawn up to mountaintops by sponge action; and on folio 11v, the salinity of springs.

Here on folio 32v, Leonardo demonstrates the synthesis achieved from his studies of the behaviour of water in nature. He describes a variety of conditions occurring at the confluence of rivers, and thereby illustrates the procedures he follows.

The discussion of the different kinds of flow in different kinds of rivers leads Leonardo to ask what would happen if the Mediterranean were to rise above its banks, and by what means water flowing into the bases of mountains rises to their summits.

On the second half of the page, he switches from effects to causes — to a geometric analysis of the transformation of water volumes that would occur in a universal flood.

The two parts considered together indicate Leonardo's foundation in Aristotelian science, which proceeds from the observation of effects in nature to the knowledge of their causes. The fundamental assumption, never open to question in Leonardo's day, is that the order of the universe can be described in Euclidean terms. Scientific knowledge is gained by finding the eternal law in geometry that explains observed phenomena.

[illegible]

[illegible]

[illegible]

[illegible]

[illegible]

Sheet 5A, folio 5r

At the top of the page, Leonardo lists the contents of his planned treatise on the science of water. The topics make up the bulk of discussion in the Codex Leicester: the nature of water in its motions, the effects of its currents, and the meeting of rivers and their ebb and flow. Leonardo describes a variety of conditions for the confluence of rivers, and thereby illustrates the procedures he follows. He saw the effects of rivers coming together, but to learn the causes of this compound motion in nature, he collected information on many different aspects of the phenomenon.

The sixth paragraph on the page concerns the moon. Here Leonardo develops details of the argument sketched on the preceding pages — that the mild radiance of the moon is due to waves moving on the surface of its watery sphere: 'And here the moon, being a spherical and opaque body, remains of uniform brightness in its parts which are apt to receive uniform light. And this, for what is said above, could not be, if water were not there; the water being spherical, it cannot receive the solar ray and reflect it to our eyes except through the ray of incidence, which is smaller in relation to the volume of the lunar body; so that, of necessity, it must be admitted that the sea waves, each for itself, take a solar ray, and the shadow interposed between the crests of the waves blends with the luminous species and does not produce such brightness as it would do were its water without waves.'

This page is also important for the information it records about Leonardo's scientific methods.

Sheet 5B, folio 5v

This and the facing page, folio 32r, study the erosion of riverbanks under various circumstances. Drawings in the margin illustrate Leonardo's geometric analyses of the effects of the movement and pressure that different water currents exert on riverbanks, as well as on any 'object placed in front of a bank'. He writes concisely, concentrating on technical engineering matters:

'Banks overflowed by rivers are affected much differently from those which are not.'

'The bottom is affected in one way by an increase of water and in another way by a decrease.'

'Objects interposed between the banks and the river course are what preserves the bank.'

'Ruins of the banks are always caused by the increase in depth at their foundations.'

'Banks split in their front collapse towards the oncoming water that percusses them.'

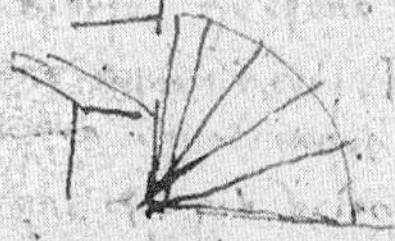

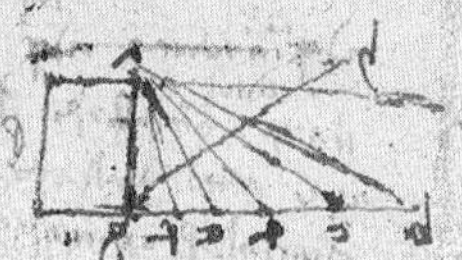

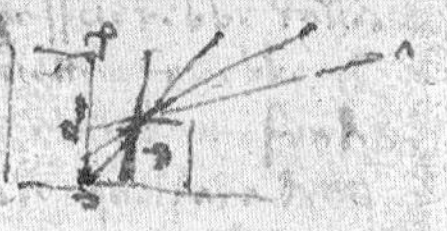

Sheet 5B, folio 32r

In the discussion of problems that erosion causes home owners who build their houses on riverbanks, Leonardo demonstrates how he has synthesised many aspects of hydraulics studied elsewhere in the codex. He devises a series of barriers and dams that move the flowing water left and right and finally deposit the eroded material 'in the hollow where your house is'.

Applying the same principle of intertwining currents of water, he creates a cascade for the steps at La Sforzesca, the luxurious country villa of his patron the duke of Milan at Vigevano.

These still-functioning steps are a tribute to Leonardo's inventiveness. They turned the potentially damaging action of rushing water to productive, aesthetically pleasing purposes.

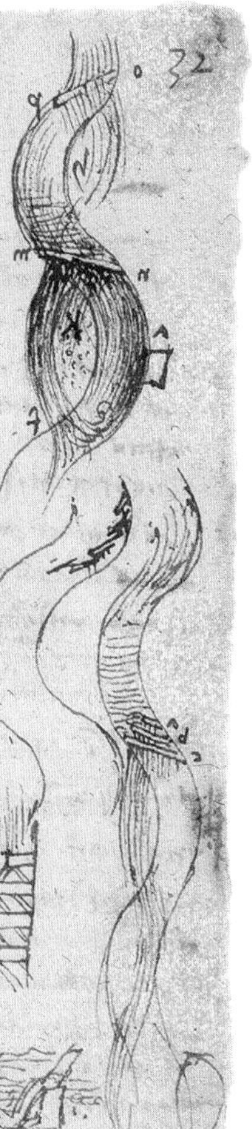

Sheet 6A, folio 31v

Only the top few lines of this page concern water, but they are enough to tie Leonardo's concerns directly to his thoughts on the body of the earth. With respect to the origin of subterranean rivers, Leonardo asks what causes the greatest variation in the tides of the sea.

Leonardo presents a brief summary of his thoughts on the circulation of water in the body of the earth, covering much of the same territory as discussions elsewhere in the codex. 'A spring may be seen in Sicily which at certain times of the year discharges chestnut leaves in large quantity. Since chestnut trees do not grow in Sicily, this spring must issue from some lake in Italy and then pass beneath the sea and afterwards find outlet in Sicily.'

He continues to reject two traditional theories accounting for the flow of water from mountaintops: one, that the seas are higher than the mountains; and the other, that the water found high on mountains originates as snow.

In the last paragraph, Leonardo describes rocks he saw on a visit to Elba in July 1503 (recorded in the Codex Madrid II). He theorises on the action of rivers wearing away rock and carrying eroded stones various distances, both into and away from the sea. 'All the outlets of waters which proceed from mountains to the sea carry stones from the mountains with them to the sea; and by the backwash of the ocean surges against their mountains, these stones were thrown back towards the mountain.'

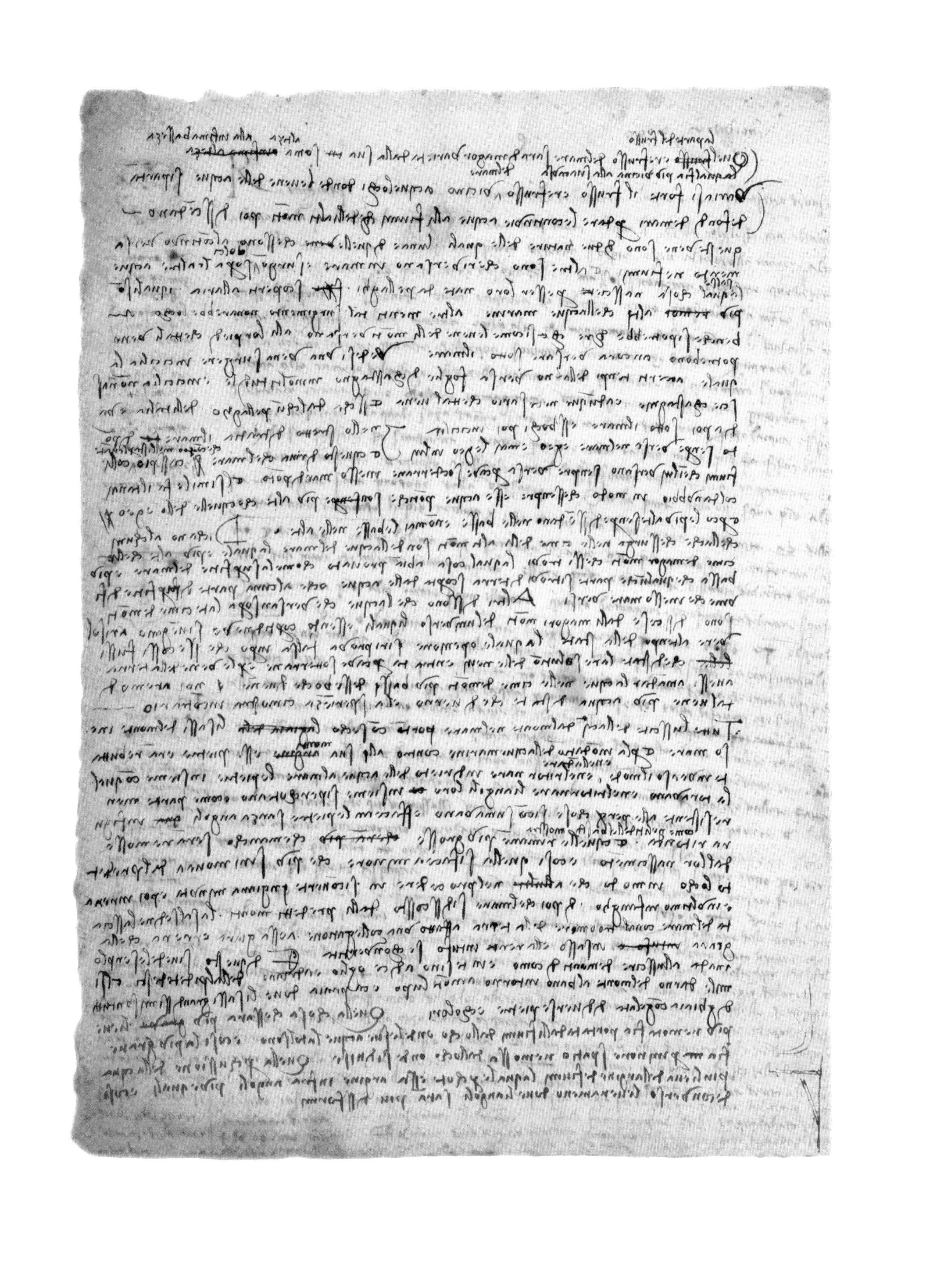

la parte del fiume [illegible] altezza alla inferiore bassezza

Quel fiume che [illegible] sarà [illegible] della sua [illegible]

Dirai forse il fiume che [illegible] acque [illegible]

[illegible] acque [illegible] fiume [illegible]

[illegible]

Sheet 6A, folio 6r

Here, as in related passages in the Codex Atlanticus, Leonardo studies the relationship between water's velocity and its pressure. He records an experiment to test the movement of water at different levels in rivers and then sets out to prove that water pressure, and therefore velocity, increases as the depth increases. He tests this hypothesis in another laboratory experiment described on folio 11r.

His approach is scientifically interesting for taking into account the complexity of forces that contribute to the flow of water. He analyses the rate of water flow at various depths in order to gauge water pressure.

He then compares the nature of moving water and still water, reasoning that still water does not exert pressure on the bottom. His evidence for this conclusion is the waving motion of the grasses that grow on the bottom and 'the very light mud at the bottom of marshes, which has almost the lightness of water itself; instead, had the water gravity over it, it would be compressed and almost petrified; the contrary being shown, the axiom that water does not weigh over its bottom is proven by the said experience.'

Leonardo concludes that water pressure must therefore be due to what he calls percussion, the impact of moving water.

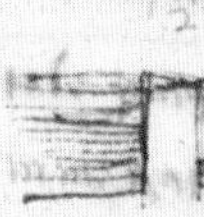

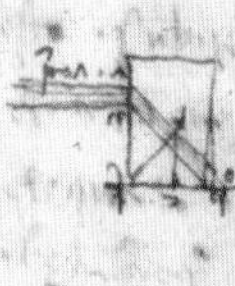

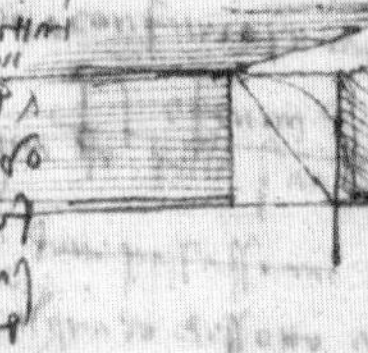

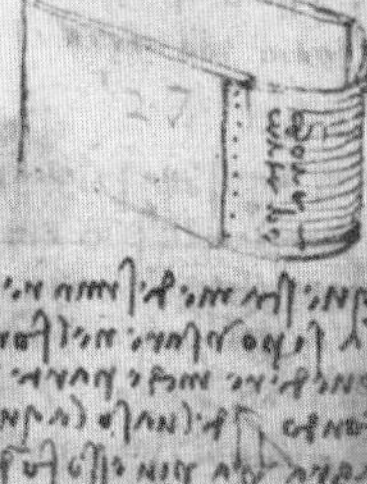

Sheet 6B, folio 6v

The ebb and flow of water both in seas and in rivers is one of Leonardo's guiding themes in the Codex Leicester. He discusses variations in the tides based on time differences around the globe: 'All seas have their flow and ebb in the same period, but they seem to vary because the days do not begin at the same time throughout the universe … When it is midday in our hemisphere, it is midnight in the opposite hemisphere.'

He also considers a number of physical variables that act upon water, including the action of the wind. He is here interested in developing measurements of the continuum of water flow and writes at length of the rush, height and weight of water and its ebb and flow.

He reveals his real interest in the discussion at the end of the page — how sediment, including shells and fossils, circulates in the body of the earth. His intuitions about the behaviour of different kinds of waterborne sediment are among the most innovative aspects of his hydrodynamic studies. This discussion, which ranges from the analysis of observable effects to general theory, shows the thoughts of Leonardo the professional hydraulic engineer in concert with his philosophical interests. He has come full cycle.

Leonardo concludes this discussion with an artistic, almost poetic observation of the origins of potter's clay: 'Nor does this remain upon the seashores, but goes back with the wave by reason of its lightness … [and] in time of calm weather it sinks down and settles on the bottom of the sea, where … it becomes compressed … and in this shells are found and this is the white earth that is used for making jugs.'

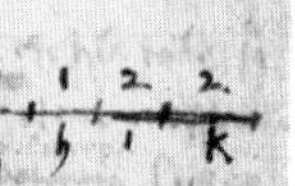
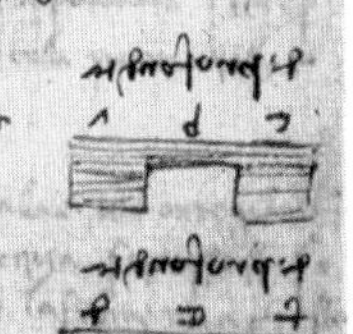

Sheet 6B, folio 31r

Leonardo continues his discussion about the circulation of water in the body of the earth. His classical sources on rivers derive from Pliny the Elder and Hercules ('Hercules came to open the sea in the west, and then the waters of the sea commenced to flow into the western ocean'), but he is indebted to Ristoro d'Arezzo for his ideas on the science of water.

On this densely written page, Leonardo takes issue with the traditional view, transmitted by Ristoro, that the seas are higher than the highest mountains. He goes on to explain at length, in technical terms, that the earth is actually a sphere and concludes: 'Many … are extremely blind who say that it is a miracle for the water in the midst of the sea to be higher than its shore … This fallacy arises from the fact that they imagine a straight line … extended above the middle of the sea, which without doubt will be higher than the shores, because the earth is a sphere and its surface forms a curve.'

Leonardo is concerned with the variable distances of seas and mountains from the centre of the earth. On folio 34v, he is concerned with theory; here, the observed action of seas and rivers is the major focus.

Leonardo's most interesting comments in the marginal notes are illustrated by diagrams of the earth. The upper right diagram shows water circulating through the earth and its return via rivers to the ocean. The lower sketch illustrates that the ocean waters are higher than the earth.

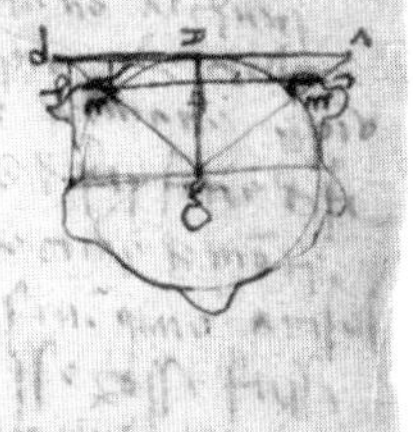

Sheet 7A, folio 30v

The configuration that interests Leonardo here is the spiral, or corkscrew. Traditionally associated with the movement of fire, which twists upward seeking its own natural level, the serpentine form was also valued artistically as the most graceful of figurative movements. Leonardo's figures and exquisite draftsmanship were particularly identified by his contemporaries with the grace of serpentine movement, which was always associated with the upward movement of the human soul seeking grace, according to a broad Neoplatonic tradition.

Here scientific cause, not Neoplatonic allegory, commands Leonardo's attention, but the modern reader cannot help but wonder at the many associations that Leonardo the artist was able to draw upon to invent and perfect his most memorable artistic images. Consider the images Leonardo weaves with his precise language in a section titled 'Of wind twists and eddies involving water': 'It often happens that, when one wind meets another at an obtuse angle, these two winds circle around together and twine themselves into the shape of a huge column, and becoming thus condensed, the air acquires weight. I once saw such winds, raging around together, produce a hollow in the sand of the seashore as deep as the height of a man, removing from it stones of a considerable size, and carrying sand and seaweed through the air for the space of a mile and dropping them in the water.'

Leonardo's illustrated discussion of the human-directed movement of water recalls the city he planned in the wake of the Milanese plague of 1483–84. (His ideas and sketches are recorded in Paris Manuscript B, circa 1487–90.) These include statements about the vigorous circulation of a healthy city: 'One needs a fast flowing river to avoid corrupt air produced by stagnation, and this will also be useful for regularly cleansing the city when opening its sluices.'

The analogy that Leonardo made between the microcosm of the human body and the macrocosm of the city is indebted to the architectural theory of Vitruvius. Many other artists drew on this theory, including Leonardo's friend Francesco di Giorgio Martini, who was also fond of analogies between macrocosm and microcosm.

The analogy between the structure of buildings and the human body is still implicit in the vocabulary of modern urban planners, who talk about roads as the arteries of cities or about a metropolis choking to death.

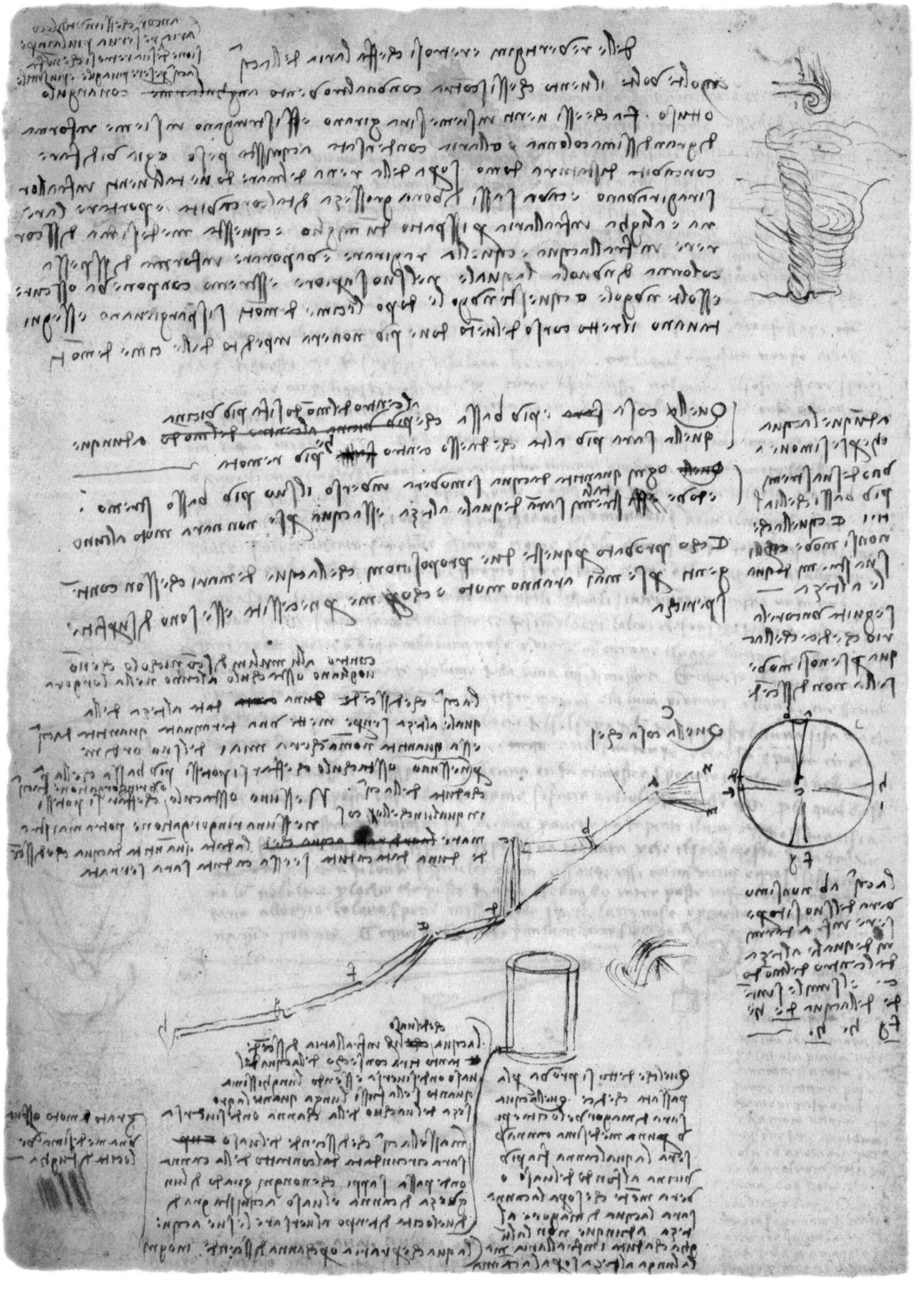

Sheet 7A, folio 7r

On this page, titled 'Of the water of the moon', Leonardo sets out to prove 'how in some aspect of the sky the shaded side of the moon has some luminosity, and how in some other part of the sky it is deprived of such luminosity'.

He notes the need to take into account the reflection of the light from the waters of the earth to explain the radiance of the moon. Later, in the sixteenth century, Galileo, who was familiar with Leonardo's manuscripts, proposed that light from neighbouring bodies affects the light of the moon. Here Leonardo claims that when the moon is at its brightest, it receives strong solar rays reflected from the earth's ocean. The argument is a good example of how Leonardo's faith in the underlying geometric structure of the universe led him to construct mental experiments based on analogies.

His proposal could not be verified, but it encouraged further speculation that countered the prevailing notion that the moon has a shiny, mirror-like surface. Here Leonardo's aim is to account for the variations in the brightness of the moon over the lunar cycle.

Near the bottom of the page he moves from his astronomical studies to bridge and weir construction. 'The pillars of bridges should always have their escarpments stretched out against the oncoming current of the rivers, otherwise the bridges will soon collapse towards the oncoming current.'

7

[illegible]

[illegible]

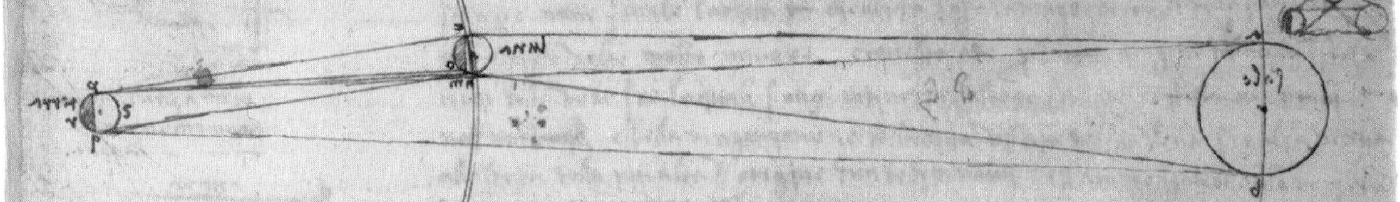

[illegible]

[illegible]

[illegible]

[illegible]

[illegible]

[illegible]

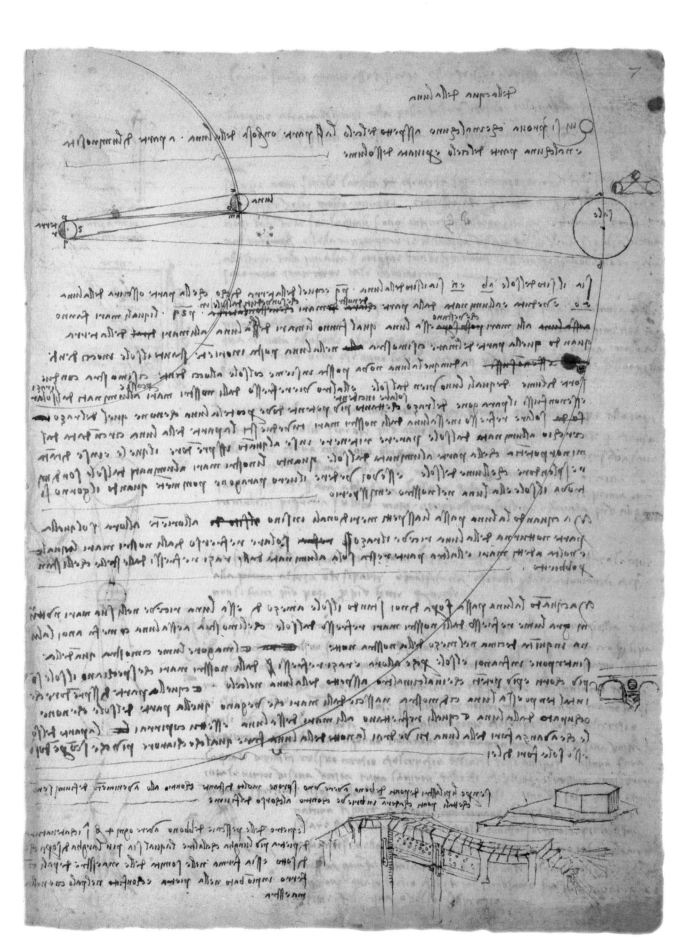

Sheet 7B, folio 7v

Leonardo here treats practical problems on the subject of rising and falling water. How does one arrange the escarpments of bridge pillars so that the current's movement won't destroy them? This question provides a context for understanding his intense interest in river currents, including the complexity of eddies and whirlpools that form around obstacles, the configurations of riverbanks, and the confluence of separate water flows.

The last paragraph on this page is about the moon. Referring to the action of light and the observer's static position, Leonardo notes that light travels in all directions, but the observer stands in one place and sees only a small part of the cosmic whole.

His logic is directed against the traditional theory that the surface of the moon is polished like a mirror. In that case, the observer would see one large reflected image. However, if the moon's surface were faceted — broken up by waves on the surface of its water — the observer would see a softer radiance, not a single, large mirror reflection of the sun.

He employs a sketch of a human eyeball between the sun and the earth to illustrate how rays of light travel and are reflected. 'But a single eye consists of a point to which the visual rays converge from the boundaries of the solar image. And as this concourse of pyramidal rays comes to be intersected by the water surface, it will show how large such an image will appear on the intersecting water surface. And the size of the intersection will be smaller the closer the eye that sees such an image is to the water surface on which the sun reflects itself.'

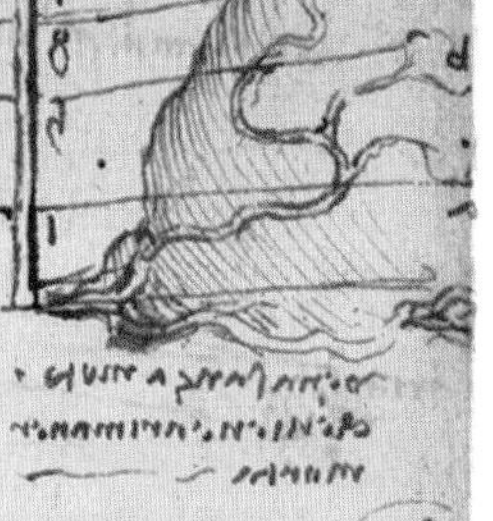

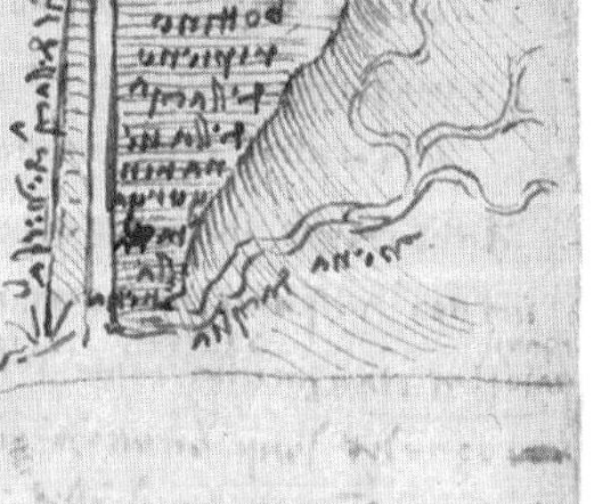

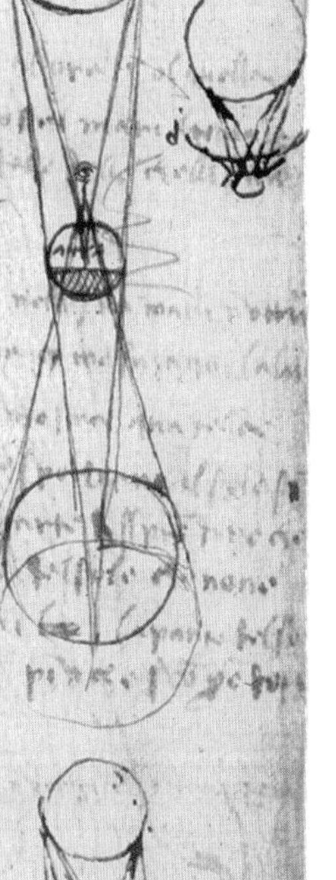

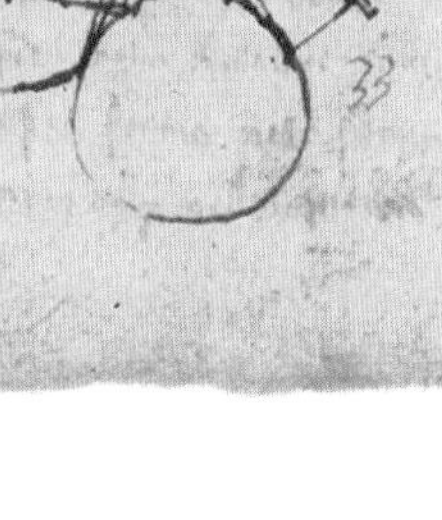

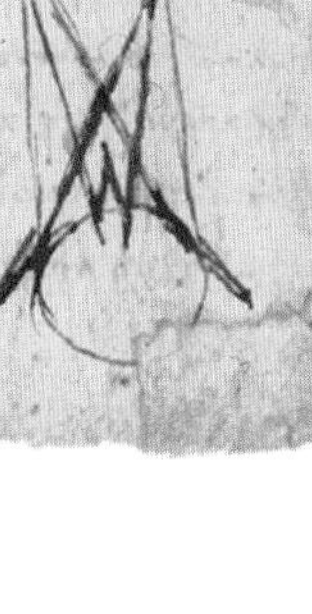

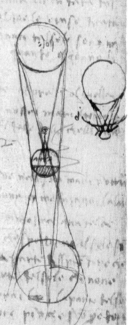

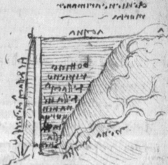

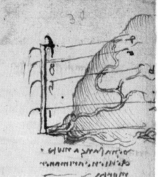

Sheet 7B, folio 30r

The arguments about the moon on this page, headed 'Of the moon', summarise in a logical order many points Leonardo has made on other pages of the codex. To his main argument that the lesser luminosity of the moon is due to the texture of its watery surface, he adds a further explanation: the moon becomes less luminous when a storm arises. 'And when the sea of the moon is stirred to tempest by the winds, the waves are larger and the lights less frequent and the enlarged shadows intermingle more with the sparse images of the sun upon the waves; and for this reason the moon becomes less luminous.'

della luna

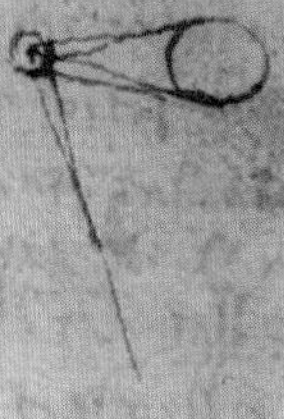

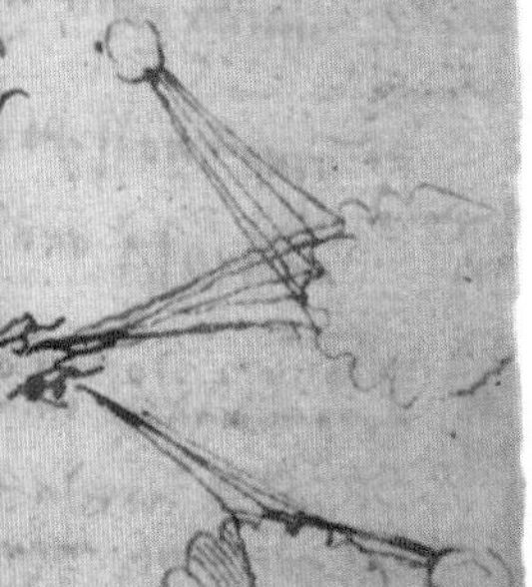

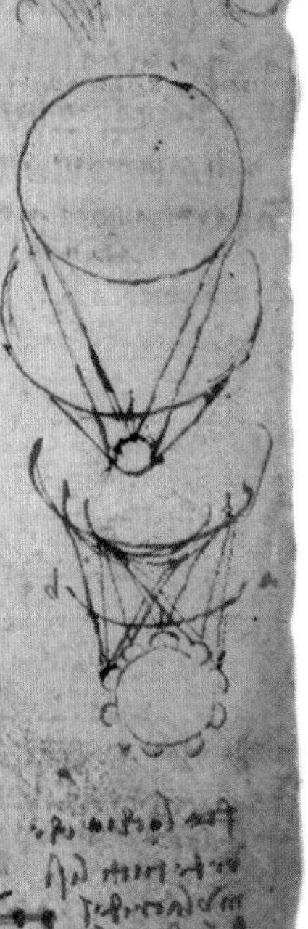

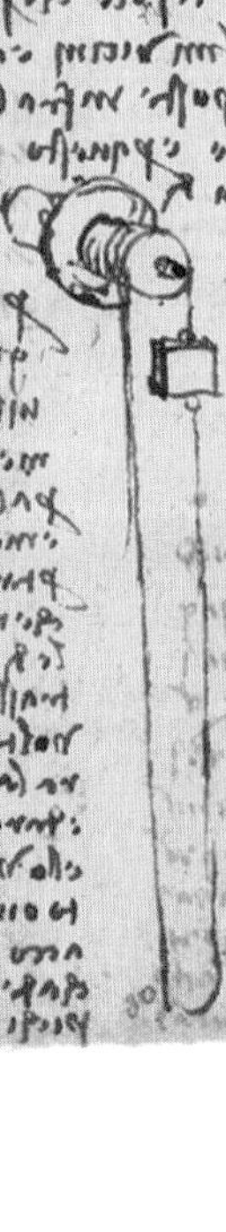

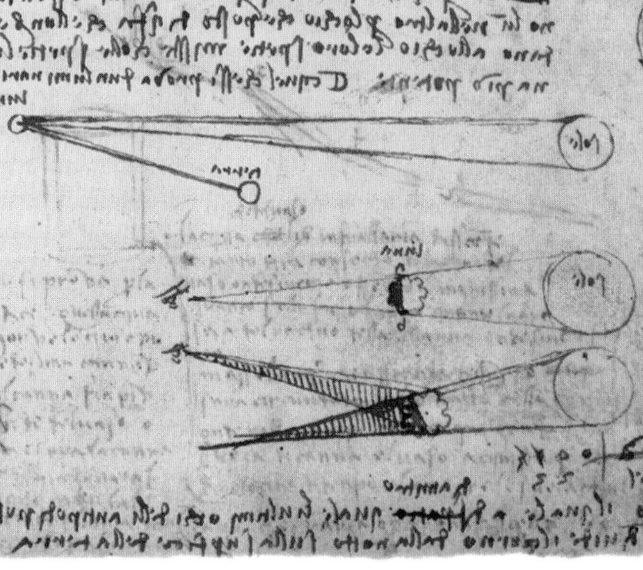

Sheet 8A, folio 29v

Here the analysis of motion continues with a classic problem drawn from the physics of the ancient Greeks.

It is also a continuation of Leonardo's discussion on the facing page, folio 8r, about the way objects move through the air. The question is whether or not air rushing into the vacuum created in the wake of a projectile pushes the projectile along its course. This concept of force was presented in Aristotle's *Physics*. Leonardo intends to reject Aristotle's theory that the cause of the motion is in the medium: 'Let it be proved how air does not push the movable object, since it is separated from the power of its mover.'

His first proof establishes conditions that remove the object, in this case a bullet, from the proposed source of its power. A bullet fired into a leather flask of water will not immediately lose its movement, as it would if the air were its sole motivator; rather, the bullet will move for quite some time after penetrating the flask. Therefore, it is not the air that provides power to the bullet.

His second argument refutes that the bullet is pushed along by the air or water filling in the vacuum behind it. Leonardo notes that the air in front of the bullet is actually more compressed than the air behind it.

Then he presents a third and final explanation, 'to which no exception can be taken. "The potency of the mover is separated from it entirely and is applied to the body moved by it, and goes on to consume itself in the course of time in penetrating the air which is always compressed before the movable object."'

For Leonardo, the action that motivates the projectile takes place in the time its flight begins and is reduced over the duration of its course. Leonardo this time counters his rhetorical adversary and lays the question to rest. Basing his argument on his direct observations of the action of water in a similar situation, he establishes by analogy that the movement of air is not necessarily what is needed to provide the force. The bullet forces the air out of its path and pushes it away. The vacuum behind it is continuously created, and the pathway is filled not by the air closest to the back, nor by that forced away from the front: 'The swift movement of the rarefied air in order to fill up the place in the vacuum, caused by the movable object departing from it, is much weaker than that which is continually being compressed before the movable object.' This analysis is correct. Leonardo notes that 'the movable object does not move on account of the wave of the air created by the impetus of the mover'.

He then anticipates the adversary's argument that 'the creasing of the air which flees before the movable object is that which prepares the movement of the movable object, together with the air which flows after it in order to restore the rarefaction of the air', meaning that the action of the air alone draws the projectile along. But Leonardo, having already shown that the air is moved aside by the bullet, not by itself, reduces this last argument to a logical quandary, pointing out that 'it is impossible that at one and the same time the mover should move the movable object and the movable object its mover'.

Leonardo's correct explanation of the motion of a projectile, contained in these few succinct phrases, is secondary to the effort he has expended to counter the arguments of a long-existing tradition.

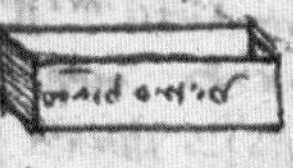

Sheet 8A, folio 8r

Leonardo here works with the principles of impetus and percussion. The page begins with a version of the axiom that water flows downhill. A passage accompanying the drawing of the seesaw discusses the effect of two men balanced on it. When one attempts to jump, they find that it requires cooperation — a stoop and jump by the first man must be coordinated with a push by the second.

This study of changing equilibrium and balance introduces a more difficult problem: How does water act when it falls (as in a waterfall) — the logical end point of water's downhill course? Leonardo is interested in explaining the causes of changing velocity. He defines the problem in Aristotelian terms as a study in compound motion. The changing velocity of falling water is due to the combination of two simple motions — flow of water downhill and pull of gravity. He explains several aspects of this compound motion, including both the increase in the force of the water as it falls and the change in the width of the stream as the water acquires velocity. Understanding this interaction requires Leonardo first to observe the effects and then to extract the principles involved.

He explains the increasing force and velocity of the water as a result of acceleration caused by gravity. But his understanding of gravity differed from ours. Leonardo inherited a concept of gravity that defined it as a force that attracts dense objects to the centre of the world. This concept was inseparable from the theory that each of the four elements has its own level or sphere, with earth, the heaviest, at the centre of the world. This central core is surrounded by the sphere of water, then air, and finally fire. Such was the makeup of the sublunary world.

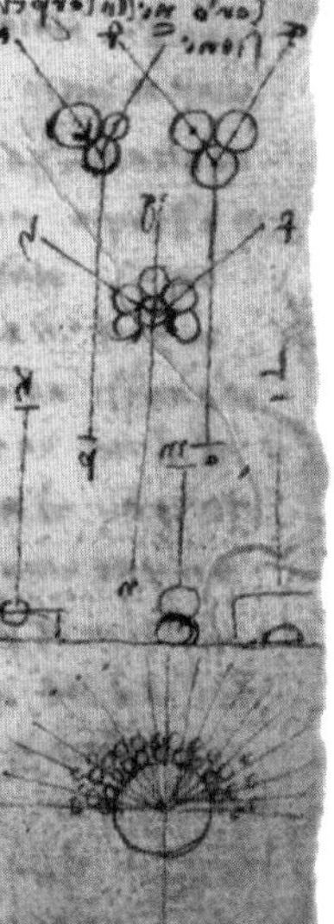

Sheet 8B, folio 8v

This is the most extensive discussion of fossils in the entire manuscript. Much space is given to countering the biblical Deluge theory as the reason that fossilised shells are found in the mountains. 'If you should say that the shells which are visible at the present time within the borders of Italy, far away from the sea and at great heights, are due to the Deluge having deposited them there, I reply that, granting this Deluge to have risen seven cubits above the highest mountain, as he has written who measured it, these shells which always stay near the shores of the sea ought to be found lying on the mountain sides, and not at so short a distance above their bases, and all at the same level, layer upon layer.'

Leonardo carefully describes the causes and effects of fast-moving water that deposits silt and other materials. The sand produces tufa stone, which incorporates marine life-forms in the location in which they lived. Successive deposits in the same place, not the Deluge, explain why the shells are produced in layers: 'And if the shells had been in the turbid water of a deluge, they would be found mixed up and separated one from another, amid the mud, and not in regular rows in layers as we see them in our own times.'

The only part of Leonardo's discussion that may confuse us today is his reference to the rising of the hemisphere when water drained out of the Mediterranean through the Strait of Gibraltar. According to the scheme of the cosmos of Leonardo's time, the elements each sought their own level. Lighter, less dense material sought a higher level than heavier, denser material. This principle applied to water too, according to Leonardo, who thought that its weight should be measured according to its depth, that is, the pressure it exerted on its base.

Sheet 8B, folio 29r

Leonardo here analyses rectilinear motion, that is, movement in a straight line, using the same vocabulary and geometry he applies to light's straight movement. In both cases, impetus mechanics is the lower, physical science that provides a model of representation for the higher, more abstract science: '"There are three aspects of the movement that water makes on being reflected from its percussion within the water penetrated by it:" the first movement is towards the bed of the water; the second is towards the place where the water is moving; the third is a whirling movement after the manner of a screw, boring continually the bank and the bed on which it rubs, and always gathering fresh force from the water that follows in succession, thrown back from the bank, which descends upon it from the air, and resubmerges it anew with itself at the bottom.'

In these circumstances it is interesting to compare the differences in Leonardo's treatment of the basic principle that the angle of incidence (the angle at which a moving force strikes a surface) is equal to the angle of reflection. With light, neither mass nor friction is involved. But the physicality of water — a medium that allows Leonardo to see its path of movement — affects the geometry. As he notes in many passages, the force of the reflected motion of water (but not of light) will always be less than the force before impact.

Sheet 9A, folio 28v

The illustrated discussion on this page is devoted to practical applications of hydraulics. Leonardo describes how to drive piles with a device that employs a man as a counterweight to raise the ram, and then how to arrange the slope of a weir so that it will not be subject to erosion.

Concerning weir construction, Leonardo says, 'In front of river dams made of hollow and spaced-out piles, a lower dam ought always to be made to a height just above water level, so that water falling from it at flood time comes to dig out the bottom and on its rebound carries with itself what it had lifted from the bottom and deposits it in front of the higher dam, providing it with a shield made of the carried material; and the water rising from that depth will reach the top of the dam from below along a slant, so that it produces no percussion or damage.'

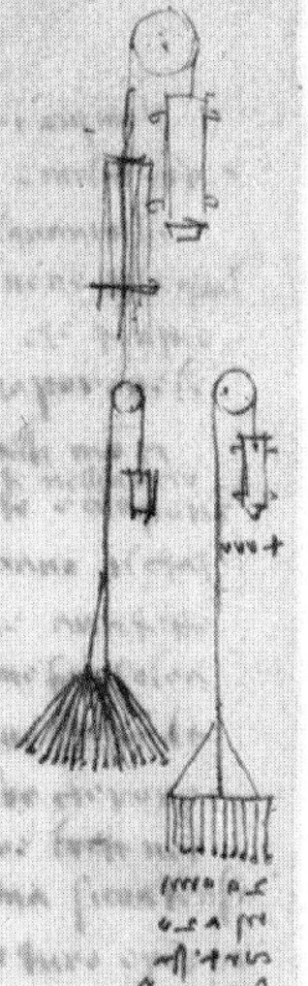

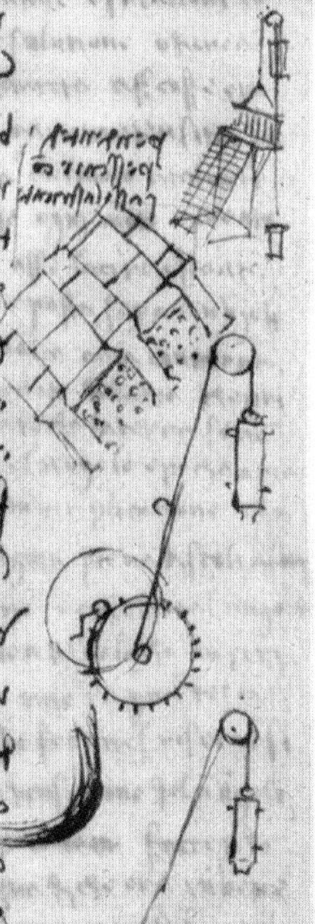

Sheet 9A, folio 9r

This page is considered to be the beginning of a compilation on water because of a note Leonardo wrote at the top: '10 sheets and 853 conclusions'.

Even though Leonardo's descriptions of locations appear to be based on actual visits, in some cases he was indebted to the written accounts of others. The present page is a good example: Giovanni Villani's *Historiae*, written in 1348, is the source of Leonardo's account of the formation of the gap at the Gonfolina rock. Villani argued that the gap was artificially made; Leonardo disagreed. He studied in detail how the churning of Deluge waters would have affected the deposit of shells and considered a variety of conditions that make water powerful. He determined to write his own book (or what would be to us a chapter) on the subject of places occupied by fresh water.

The discussion here concerns the problem, frequently encountered in the codex, of accounting for the presence of shells on mountaintops. Leonardo the hydraulic engineer draws from his own experience: 'A great quantity of shells may be seen where the rivers empty themselves into the sea.' Citing two examples — the rivers of the Apennines, which empty into the Adriatic, and the Arno tumbling from the rock of Gonfolina — he concludes that the shells in the mix of fresh and salt water came down the rivers from the mountains.

'The waters which came from the earth to the sea, although they drew the sea towards the earth, were those which smote its base, because water which comes from the earth has a stronger current than the sea, and as a consequence is more powerful and enters beneath the other water of the sea, and stirs up the bottom and carries with it all the movable objects which are to be found in it, such as the above-mentioned shells and other like things; and as water which comes from the land is muddier than that of the sea, it is so much the more powerful and heavier than it. I do not see therefore in what way the said shells could have come to be so far inland unless they had been born there.'

The last part of the page advises how to set wooden bridge timbers at a slant to avoid the direct impact of cut logs floating downriver into them.

Sheet 9B, folio 9v

Throughout this page, Leonardo uses logic, observation and experimentation to understand the phenomenon of fossils as part of the natural world and not as remnants of a biblical event. 'And we find oysters together in very large families, among which some may be seen with their shells still joined together, which serves to indicate that they were left there by the sea and that they were still living when the Straits of Gibraltar were cut through.' This key passage implies an alternative, cyclical theory for the composition of the body of the earth in regard to the presence of seashells on mountaintops. Leonardo argues that they were left behind when the Mediterranean drained from its formerly higher level.

To further explore the origins of the mountain shells, he describes and diagrams two tests in a glass-walled tank he calls a pit. The ability to observe the action of water through a glass pane allowed Leonardo a much better understanding of the medium than he could gain by watching random acts of nature. One test is designed to show what effect wind has on an object floating submerged within the water. The other is 'to see whether the small surface wave causes the water to move high above its bottom'. Both are intended to demonstrate that neither the action of wind nor waves could have washed the shells up the mountain slopes during the Deluge. This problem is central to his theory about the composition of the body of the earth.

In conjunction with these laboratory experiments, in 1508 Louis XII, the king of France, gave Leonardo a stretch of the Naviglio Grande Canal in Milan for his hydraulic experiments.

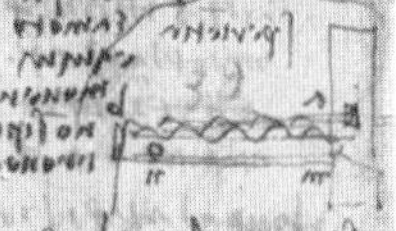

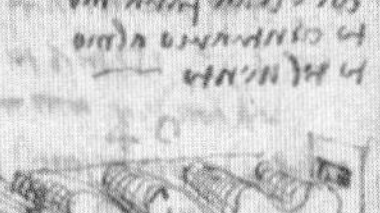

Sheet 9B, folio 28r

Although it has only one illustration, this page presents one of the most vivid images in the entire codex. Leonardo begins by comparing the earth's and animals' branching circulation systems, and then describes weather as a system of condensation and evaporation of water that creates clouds and hurricanes. In lucid detail he describes his observation of the formation of a thunderhead and records an idea for measuring wind and water speeds by using a waterwheel.

This page also embodies one of Leonardo's most comprehensive treatments of the macrocosm in terms of the four elements. In fact, the action of water in particular epitomises the entire treatise. On the facing page, folio 9v, he suggests a cyclical theory for the circulation of water in the body of the earth. Here he suggests the alternative theory that the seas drain into caverns, which erode much as riverbanks do. This erosion has caused more water to pour from the body of the earth than in former times, and the seas are lower than they used to be.

This discussion of water gives way to a consideration of how the element of fire, in the form of heat, is part of the system of the earth's body. Then Leonardo considers air, in the form of wind.

[illegible]

[illegible]

Sheet 10A, folio 27v

At the top of the page, Leonardo's discussion of the evaporation of moisture is directly related to the experiment that he describes on the facing page, folio 10r. Here he makes a connection with the theory that the circulation of water inside the body of the earth is due to its being vaporised in caverns. His considerations of earthquakes make sense in that context: 'The rumbling produced by the earthquake in the body of the earth proceeds from the destruction of places torn open by force by the winds which continually strike upon the beds of their great caverns or lakes, covered and shut within the earth.'

The second passage concerns the varying directions of water movement at differing depths. The subject seems, at first reading, unrelated to the discussion on the rest of this page and the facing page, but its continuation on folio 10v clarifies the connection: Leonardo is concerned with the formation of strata, which, in part, accounts for the presence of marine fossils on mountaintops. Leonardo was aware, from his reading of the works of Ristoro d'Arezzo and other historical accounts, that solving this particular problem was an important contribution to any successful explanation of the composition of the world.

'At Bordeaux … the sea rises about 40 braccia before it ebbs, and the salt waters flood the river for more than 150 miles; and the vessels … are left high and dry on the top of a high hill above where the sea has receded … Above Tunis there is the greatest ebb in the Mediterranean Sea, namely about 2 braccia and a half; and at Venice the fall is 2 braccia, and in the other parts of the Mediterranean Sea the fall is little or nothing … The river Po will cause the Adriatic Sea to dry up in the same way it has dried up a great part on Lombardy.'

The third passage on the page, also continued on the opposite side of the sheet, concerns various ways of controlling the movement of water. Here Leonardo concentrates on the twisting action of water.

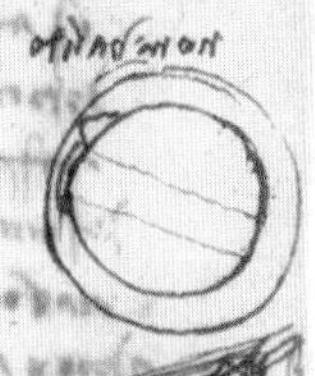

Sheet 10A, folio 10r

Consisting almost entirely of text, this page contains only two illustrations. A close look at the handwriting, colour of ink, and width of Leonardo's pen allows us to see the order in which he recorded his ideas. This textual evidence also suggests the relationship of various subjects to one another and to the history of Leonardo's received ideas. The handwriting and ideas discussed here corroborate each other very well.

The main text concerns the formation of mountains. Leonardo considers various methods of soil movement and focuses on the strata of rocks. He is concerned with accounting for the presence of shells and other marine life in rock strata at high altitudes and, in a personal outburst, takes issue with those who contradict his scientific theories.

In the right margin, Leonardo describes an experiment related to the discussion of the evaporation of moisture that appears on the top of folio 27v. Leonardo suggests a measurement to determine the expansion ratio of water to steam and draws an apparatus consisting of a membranous sack half-filled with air and set into an open-topped tank on a stand, below which a fire burns. Upon the sack rests a counterweighted board. As the water in the sack is heated and steam fills the empty half, the board is lifted to the top of the tank. Leonardo proposes to measure the change in the level of tank water after the steam fills the sack.

Although this seems a straightforward experiment, it is doubtful that Leonardo ever carried it out, since the expansion ratio of steam to water is 1,600:1, and the mathematics do not compute. On folio 15r, another series of drawings shows variations of this proposal. The great difference between the volume of water and that of steam represents a continuing flaw in Leonardo's thought experiments, one that seems inherited from his predecessors. On this page we can see Leonardo adjusting the design of the experiment to gain the results he wanted.

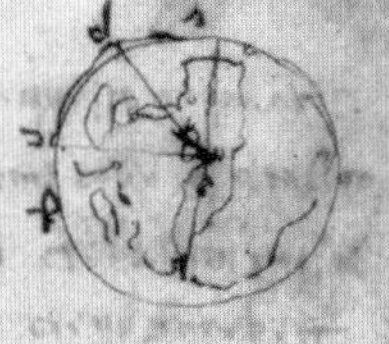

Sheet 10B, folio 10v

The first paragraph on this page follows from an observation of waves at different depths described on folio 27v. The connecting link to this and to a similar passage on folio 10r is the composition of rock strata, one of Leonardo's passions.

'And if you should say that it was the Deluge that carried these shells away from the sea for hundreds of miles, this cannot have happened, for the Deluge came about as the result of rains, because rains naturally cause rivers together with the objects carried by them to rush towards the sea, and they do not draw up to the mountains the dead things on the seashores.'

In a wide-ranging rumination about the Deluge, Leonardo cites a variety of physical evidence from his own experience to confute the biblical account as the reason that seashells and marine fossils are found on the tops of mountains. His contemporary evidence includes the earthquake of 1489 'in the sea of Satalia near to Rhodes, and it opened the depths of the sea … And above the plains of Italy where flocks of birds are flying today, fishes were once moving in large shoals.'

The lower half of the page continues the discussion on the cohesion of water drops under various conditions that begins at the top of folio 27r. Here on folio 10v, Leonardo begins with the natural causes that form the earth's topography and finishes with a practical engineering application: how to place piles in rivers so that the eroding waters do not destroy retaining walls. Leonardo explores this hydraulic question through an analysis of the mechanics of water movement.

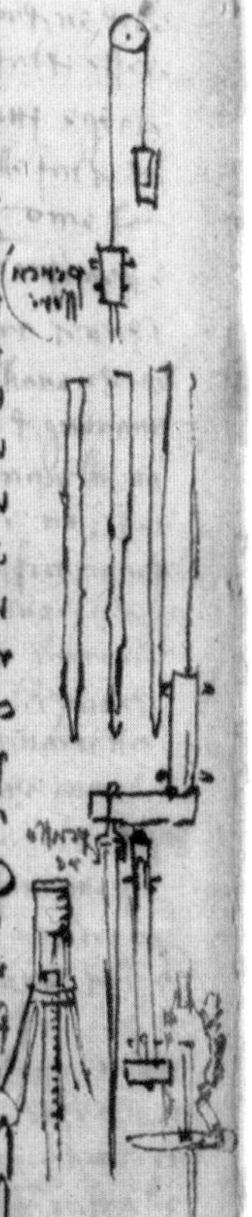

Sheet 10B, folio 27r

Leonardo describes the action of water at the nearly microscopic level of a falling drop. The drop provides an apt analogy to the 'watery sphere' of the earth. 'That water may have tenacity and cohesion together is quite clearly shown in small quantities of water, where the drop, in the process of separating itself from the rest, before it falls becomes elongated as possible, until the weight of the drop renders the tenacity by which it is suspended so thin that this tenacity, overcome by the excessive weight, suddenly yields and breaks and becomes separated from the drop, and returns upward contrary to the natural course of its gravity, nor does it move from there ... until it is again driven down by the weight which has been reformed.'

This continues a topic begun on folio 34v, where Leonardo describes the changing shape of a dewdrop as it increases in size. Here he focuses on the action of water and its cohesive properties, listing twenty-three different cases of cohesion. These include the action of water passing through felt and air. 'The same is seen with water passed through felt, for the greater weight of water that is outside the vessel draws back the lesser weight of water which this folded felt holds back within the vessel.'

Leonardo's line of thinking regarding different materials through which water passes involves his inherited concept of continuous and discontinuous quantities. This terminology originated with Aristotle, who described geometry as dealing with all physical matter 'continuous' in nature. He applied the term 'discontinuous' to arithmetical constructs. Leonardo is concerned with quantifying physical matter — how to measure it in discrete, or discontinuous, units.

He gives a list of topics dealing with circumstances that produce different movements of water. His interest in cataloguing seems to originate from a fascination with different patterns in water.

Leonardo's abiding concern with the problem of the earth's body is most apparent towards the end of the passage, where he discusses the action of water in siphons.

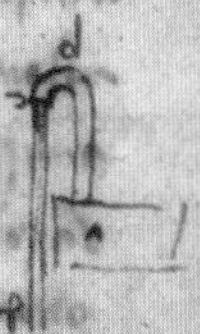

Sheet 11A, folio 26v

Leonardo notes in his own hand at the top of this page that 'in these eight sheets there are 730 conclusions pertaining to water'. This suggests to scholars that these sheets form the core of Leonardo's treatise on water.

The illustrated discussion of somersaulting waves hitting the shore leads Leonardo to the conclusion that it is not possible to describe the movement of water without first defining gravity, how the movement is created, and how it dies. Indeed, pre-Newtonian concepts of gravity, wedded to theories of the four elements central to the analogy between macrocosm and microcosm, were problematic for Leonardo.

He illustrates Aristotle's concept of continuous quantity with the proposition that a wine-filled vessel to which water is added will always contain some wine because 'as it can be divided to infinity, this continuous quantity of wine will be divided into an infinite number of hours; and because the infinite has no end in time, there will be no end to the number of parts into which the wine will be divided'. This example comes from Heron of Alexandria, Leonardo's source for a number of experiments and machines.

Leonardo's description of the reflex action of a wave striking the shore and bounding back to sea, another example of continuous quantity, anticipates the first documented scientific explanation by Christian Huygens in 1673. The circular motion Leonardo saw in waves and clouds is indebted to the ancient theory of antiperistasis. Greek philosophers since Plato (in *Timaeus*) gave pre-eminence to circular motion, which ultimately represented the harmony of the universe, or dynamic balance, created by the Prime Mover.

At the end of this page, Leonardo reaches a paradoxical conclusion that denies the influence of the moon on the tides. 'Of the flow and ebb of the sea and how the moon does not cause it ... Here is the moon, then, which moves the sea water 916 ⅔ miles in ... six hours ... and the sea water in such a period of time is not seen to move; thus it is not moved by the moon, but is sucked up by the earth.'

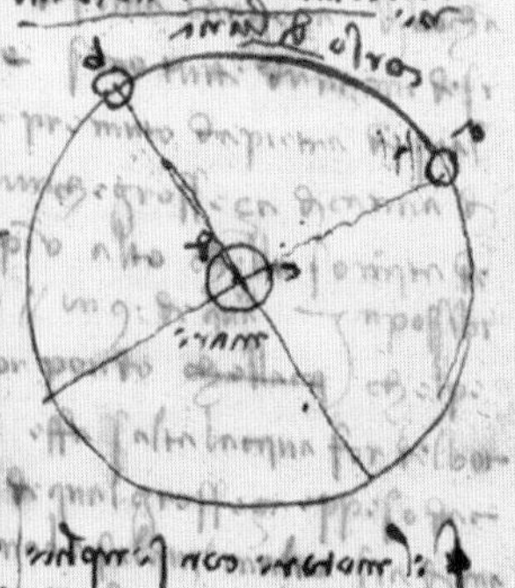

Sheet 11A, folio 11r

One of the main problems Leonardo treated in his studies of hydraulics was how water acquires power in proportion to its velocity. His discussion here includes an experiment about water pressure, illustrated in the margin by a drawing of a device that prophetically resembles a kind of coffee maker in use today. Although he leaves out the element of heat or fire, Leonardo's description of this device sounds curiously similar to a modern espresso machine: 'The mouth of the pipe which pours the water pressed out of a vessel will have such proportion to the total amount of the vacuum of its vessel, as the weight of the water which is found in the pipe, and which is brought up above all the water left in the vessel, has to the weight pressing over the vessel.'

He continues with a discussion of measuring that water pressure, referring to the storage of wine in barrels, and theorises that the weight of the water at the bottom of a barrel is quite heavier than that at the top: 'Water in itself gives more weight to the hole made at the bottom of the vessel than water does at the surface, and at every degree of depth it acquires degrees of weight; and the proof is seen in the wine casks.'

He adds a direct admonishment to readers about his final draft: 'See to it that the examples and the proofs that have to be given in this work be stated and defined before you present them.'

Leonardo proceeds with an example of the measurement of pressure. 'The air that fills a ball has power uniformly distributed within the ball, although, mathematically speaking, it should be heavier at the bottom than at the surface because "Compressed air acquires weight within the air which is not compressed, and more so at the lower than at the upper support."'

He then reveals a vivid analogy between the explosion of a natural, water-based fumarole, or geyser, and that of a man-made, gunpowder-based bombard, or mortar. 'Water overcome by the heat in the bowels of the earth evaporates and increases in volume, similarly to gunpowder ignited in a bombard, and it splits the earth open where it is weaker, and it puffs out at intervals because it is constrained by the weight of the earth, which had opened up to give way to its first impulse; and when the impetus of an exit is lacking, the impetus of the weight prevails and shuts the opening, hence the building up of steam pressure again, which again causes the earth to split open suddenly.'

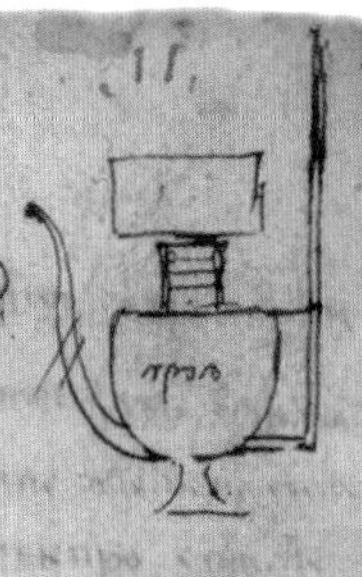

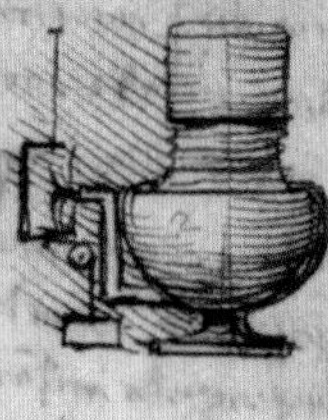

Sheet 11B, folio 11v

On this unillustrated page, Leonardo describes the veins of the earth as the places where both salt and fresh waters are found and speculates on how they are joined at the bottom of the seas: 'How many veins of salt water are found at great distance from the sea: and this may have come about because these veins have passed through some mine of salt ... where salt is hewn out of immense quarries just as blocks of stone are. How within rocks surrounded by salt waters and within these salt waters themselves in the same way there rise in many places veins of fresh water ... How the sea waters pick up the saltiness from the salt mines which are spread all over the bottom of the sea and which dissolve in water. How on the bottom of the sea there is fresh water; and this I have ascertained personally. How all the active veins, ramified and woven into the body of the earth, are joined with the bottom of the sea.'

He interweaves an observation on the phenomenon of underwater springs, citing a location he had visited: 'How there are in many places veins of water which rise for six hours and sink for six hours; and I have myself seen one above Lake Como, called Plinian Fountain, which increases and decreases in this way to such an extent that when it flows it drives several mills, and when it falls it falls so low that it is as though one were looking at the water in a deep well.'

Leonardo also discusses the relationship of surface waves to the sea bottom and to the shore. The point of this discussion would seem to be to describe the way viscosity affects wave action.

[illegible]

Sheet 11B, folio 26r

On this page Leonardo describes a number of practical applications of the theoretical study of water pressure, particularly as it applies to swamp drainage. Here, as elsewhere, he lists a number of 'cases', in this instance eighteen, to be examined in the future.

Leonardo begins the page with directions on how to empty a swamp by means of 'siphonic action' and ends with a sketch about the weight of water in a cylindrical container upon which he has marked off measurements similar to those on a modern measuring cup. His conception, however, is somewhat different from ours: he assumes that the water at the bottom of the container is 'heavier'. We would say it is under greater pressure from the column of water above it.

Drafts of the passages included here appear in the Codex Atlanticus. The physical evidence indicates that Leonardo kept the information for that codex on loose sheets stacked one inside the other. The Codex Leicester probably originated the same way.

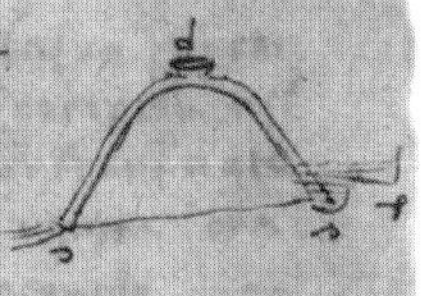

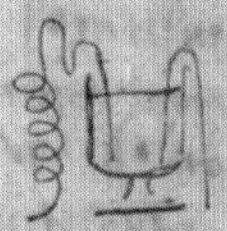

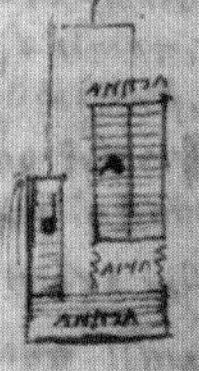

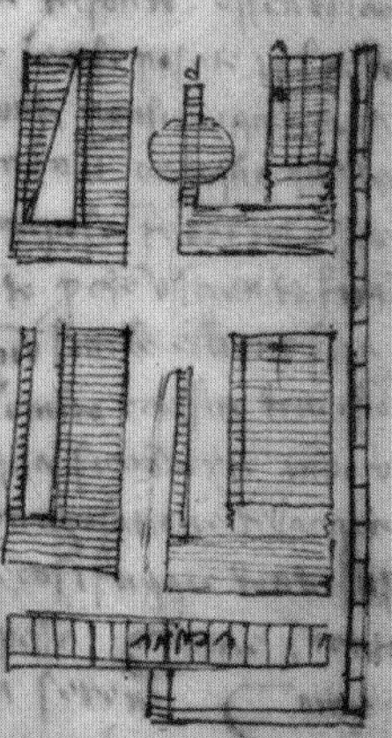

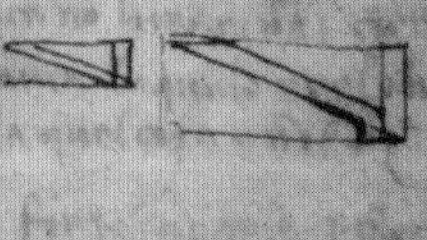

Sheet 12A, folio 25v

Most of this page, which at the top announces fifteen cases to be considered in the future, deals with the movement of water. Leonardo's studies of compound motion here analyse the shapes and patterns that result from the confluence of water meeting from different directions. He considers factors of depth, percussion (impact), and velocity.

Much of this material detailing examinations of eddies and whirlpools formed in water has been dealt with on other pages. Leonardo's illustrations here are some of the most beautiful of the codex. The vortices formed by water, the curling wave action, the separation of currents caused by obstacles placed in the water's flow, all exhibit a careful observation of nature.

The page ends with a comparison of the movements that result when water percusses air and sand.

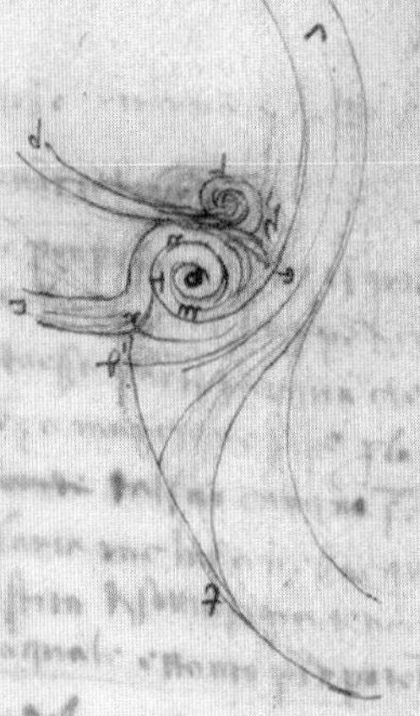

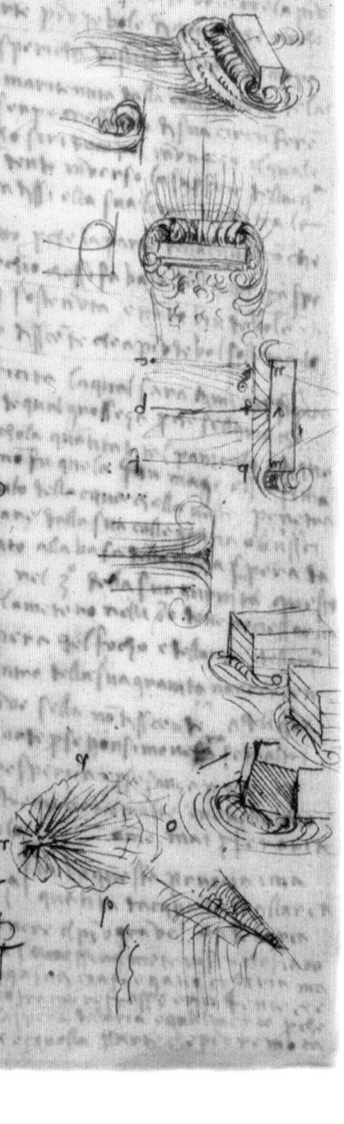

Sheet 12A, folio 12r

The heading on this page, 'In these seven sheets are 657 cases pertaining to water and its bottom', has been the subject of scholarly speculation about the organisation of the treatise.

Here Leonardo discusses the flow of water in every conceivable situation — through floodgates, down waterfalls, against the shore, from the surface to the depths of rivers. He is especially interested in the reflex action after impact: 'The reflex motion of water is much slower than the incident motion because the percussion of the reflex water takes place in water of little motion in the sea, and the sea does not empty the waters with that speed with which they come to it, and it therefore makes a new reflection against the first reflex motion.'

It is interesting to note here a comparison of Leonardo's discussion of water and light with impetus mechanics, the science that provided him with a model for analysing the process of motion in a straight line. In the case of light, there is no need to consider diminished force after impact. In the case of water, however, the mass of the liquid involves physics, and the angle of reflection is always diminished.

Although most of this page considers the movement of water, the first paragraph and the beautiful illustrations in the margin deal with gravity and are directly related to the problem of the body of the earth.

Leonardo diagrams a method for dividing the mass of an asymmetrical object. He proposes to suspend two objects from a single point so that their centres are the same distance from the point of suspension. If the two objects are the same weight, they will touch each other at a theoretical vertical line drawn down from the point of suspension. If they are unequal, the heavier object will shift over that line to a degree determined by the total weight of the two objects.

In the illustrated case, the heavier object weighs three pounds and the lighter just one, for a combined weight of four pounds. Two pounds lie to the left and two to the right of the plumb line, an equal division of their total mass but an asymmetrical division of the three-pound object. Leonardo claims that this empirical method for dividing irregular objects 'never fails'.

This thought experiment is an application of the idea of accidental gravity to determine the point of equilibrium of the two suspended balls.

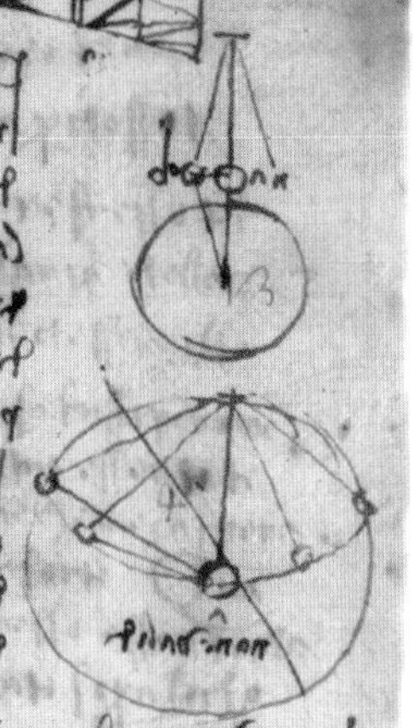

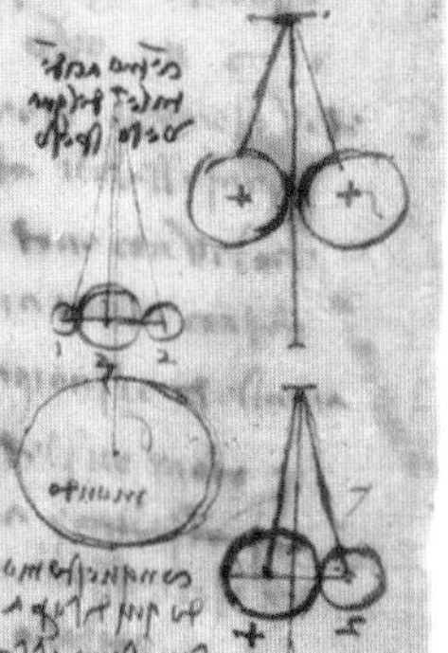

Sheet 12B, folio 12v

While not directly concerned with the theme of the body of the earth, Leonardo's considerations here are much clearer if we keep in mind that the four elements are essential to theories of the macrocosm.

Leonardo explores the interrelationships of three of the four elements — air, water and fire — both visually and through thought experiments. He begins with a simple observation on the pattern of surface waves in a bowl of water. The last example on the page concerns not water but air. Leonardo writes that smoke, like water, moves at first fast, and then more slowly because 'it becomes colder and heavier, owing to the fact that a great part of it is condensed through the parts striking against each other and being pressed together and made to adhere one to another'.

Leonardo's comparison of the elements is made explicit in the text where he mentions Heron of Alexandria's steam-driven rotating ball, the Eolipile, as a demonstration of applied pressure created by heat. He compares this to the action of wind striking a mountain peak, illustrated at the bottom of the page.

Three points may be made about this discussion as a whole: First, Leonardo is looking for ways to describe rates of change for two variables. His method of quantification is rooted in geometric ratios, not absolute units of measurement. Second, the underlying scheme for his structural analogy of air and water is the four elements. And third, his accounts of the behaviour of particles suspended in a medium were unprecedented. The subject is still a challenge in the modern science of fluid dynamics.

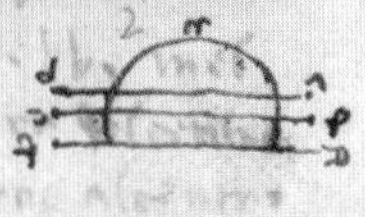
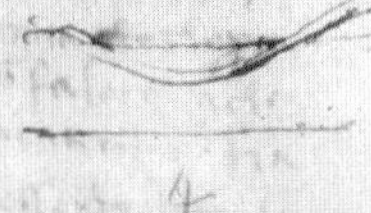

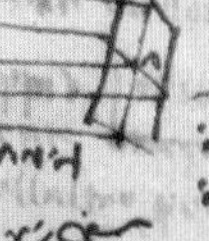
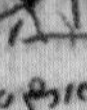

Sheet 12B, folio 25r

'12 cases … These are cases that have to be placed at the beginning.'

Leonardo presents an argument about the circulation of water through the earth similar to the one on folio 21v, where the emphasis is on the movement of water. The cases listed here begin with discussions on the interaction of air and water and introduce the subsequent development of his theories.

Leonardo returns to the problem at the heart of his exploration of the body of the earth — accounting for the way that water rises to the tops of mountains. He disagrees with those who contend that the oceans are higher than the mountain peaks: 'That part of water is higher which is more remote from the centre of the sphere of fire and of the air and of the water, but not of the earth, because this has not a mathematical spherical shape.'

The direct use of mathematical concepts, like the one about the geometry of the earth just described, helps to clarify the particular language Leonardo employs both here and at the end of the argument: 'Water of itself does not move unless it descends: therefore, when it is in its sphere it does not have one part of itself lower than another, and therefore it will not move of itself unless something else moves it; and the two aforesaid proofs are sufficient to prove that water is spherical and of itself without movement; and as a consequence all the waters that move of themselves are lower at one extremity than at the other — that is, in their surface; so finding the descent, it flows there because there is no support for it there.'

Leonardo's analysis of the geometry of these configurations could almost be compared to the visual narratives of his artistic composition. Another aspect is the argument he uses: a series of linked axioms that lead to a geometric proof. Leonardo adapts this form of argument to his investigations into the nature of water as a part of the entire system of the body of the earth.

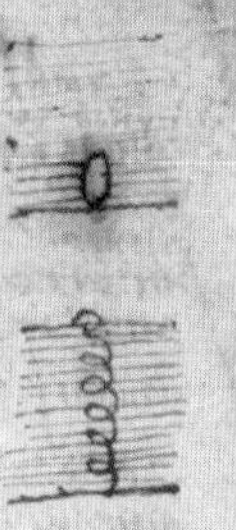

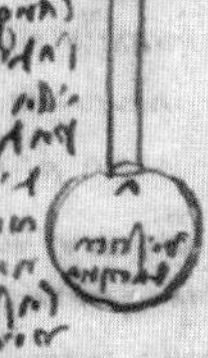

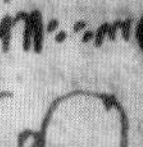

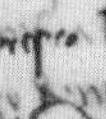

Sheet 13A, folio 24v

Here, in one of the most practical sections of the codex, Leonardo explores the issues affecting water travel from the boatman's point of view. He opens the section with a very general text on the effects of floods on river bottoms and some observations on the tides and coastal currents in the area.

He provides practical drawings and written notes and links his hydraulic theories with practice on the water. He discusses how to read the water's surface and currents to learn about sand deposits and depth for navigation and how to recognise submerged sandbanks at sea from some distance away.

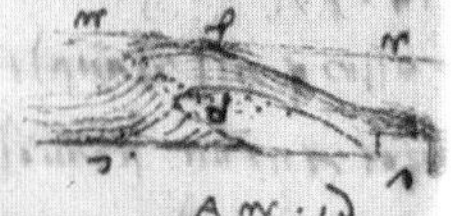

Sheet 13A, folio 13r

In the text at the upper left, Leonardo cites a lost work on ships by Leon Battista Alberti and *On Aqueducts*, by the Roman writer Frontinus. He continues to work with the accepted ideas and writings of the time but explores their conclusions in his own ways.

On this page Leonardo gives a description of a seagoing clock and tells of ways to measure the course and speed of a ship. At first glance, these seem out of place in the codex, but actually they are the keys to understanding that sheet 13 is intended as a practical guide for seamen. His descriptions of the relationship between surface patterns and the river bottom anticipate by 500 years the lessons learned by young Samuel Clemens (Mark Twain) in *Life on the Mississippi*, particularly the opening of chapter nine.

While learning the river, Clemens is told: 'You are well up on the bar now; there is a bar under every point, because the water that comes around it forms an eddy and allows the sediment to sink. Do you see those fine lines on the face of the water that branch out like the ribs of a fan? Well those are little reefs.'

Leonardo writes: 'Where a reflected current meets its own waves in the stream, the water will always be shallow, because in such a spot a sharp-crested heap of sand is created, the slopes of which are affected by the friction of two contrary motions ... When the surface of the water consists of small shaded waves which form themselves into lines that meet at an angle, the fact shows that the bed of the river is not deep, and it is also produced by the sand thrown off by the water as it passes through a confined space such as the arch of a bridge or the like.'

Practical ability for the pilot of a boat, no matter what the river, involves being able to discern what lies below the water's surface.

The upper illustrations show a geometric method for determining the speed of a boat. The centre drawings illustrate the underwater vortices created when something blocks the current. The lower drawing shows the course of the Arno at four different points on its route towards Florence.

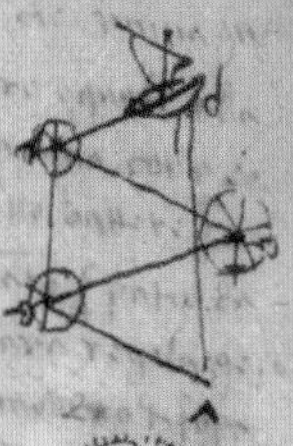
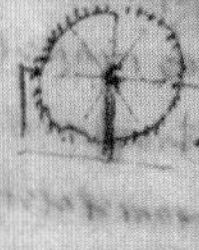

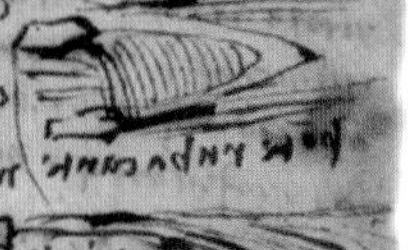

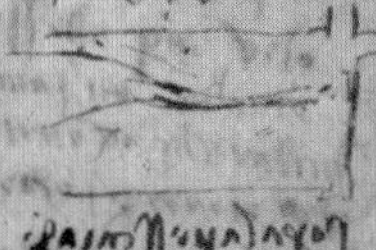
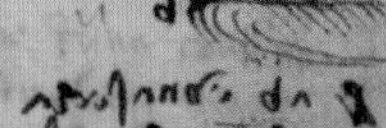

Sheet 13B, folio 13v

Leonardo continues his discussion of controlling the flow of rivers, and he gives indications here that his observations involve more than just watching a river from a boat. In one passage he proposes an accurate method of gauging the speed of a current. In his time there was no concept of a second hand or a stopwatch. To measure a short-term event such as the passage of an object bobbing in a swift current, one normally counted the beats of one's own pulse. Leonardo, an accomplished musician, decided that the beat of musical measure — which he defines on folio 6v as 1,080 units per hour — would be more regular. With his usual resourcefulness, Leonardo invents standard measures to quantify his studies of nature.

He adds another dimension of scientific precision to his study of water when he includes controlled experiments, such as 'how a small weight close to the bottom of transparent water, suspended by a thread from a float, may explain the varieties of the motions below the surface of the water'.

Leonardo recognises not only the relationship between the surface of water and its bottom but also the need to clearly understand the workings of the intervening column of fluid. This program of study is one that any modern hydraulic engineer would recognise, as it involved the creation of glass-sided tanks that allowed him to observe and control as many conditions as possible.

His last idea on the page addresses avoiding or reducing the effects of erosion: 'When one wants to extinguish such power which causes the hollowing out of a riverbed, one ought to order a transverse current directed against such clashing of the waters, so as to hit them and set them apart, and to spread and weaken them.'

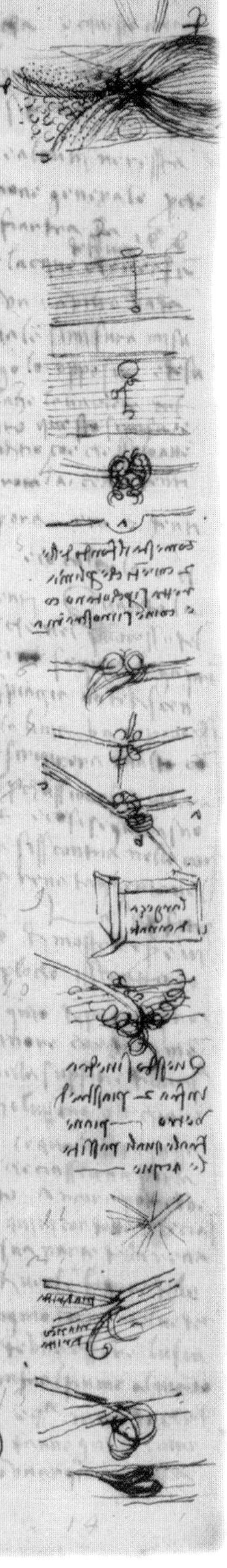

Sheet 13B, folio 24r

Leonardo offers a generalised discussion on maintenance and control of a river: 'It is possible to devise obstacles that will protect the riverbanks against the friction of the water current.' This is the most important statement on this page. Leonardo proposes establishing a practical branch of engineering dedicated to the creation and use of obstacles to control the flow of a river and the deposition of sediment.

His plan is to shift the main current of the river towards the middle of its channel to protect its banks. His drawings are meant to show how currents of water are affected by well-placed impediments to their flow.

Leonardo often relates small and large events of the same nature and explores the differences: 'How the swollen waters of great floods make the same revolutions in their occurrences as do the small waters in their own; but the water engaged in the small one, which is little, makes little movement from the upper to the lower part of its wave; and that same quantity of water, in the very great wave, makes great movement, so that it is no longer to be seen as transparent water, but it turns into smoke or mist, or foam, on account of its great revolution.'

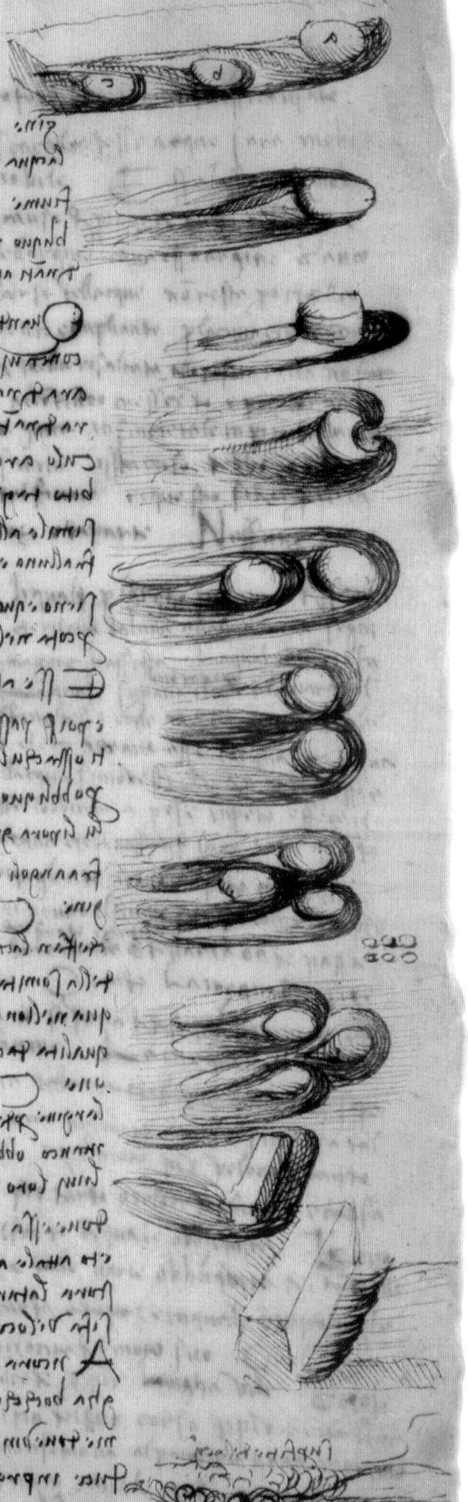

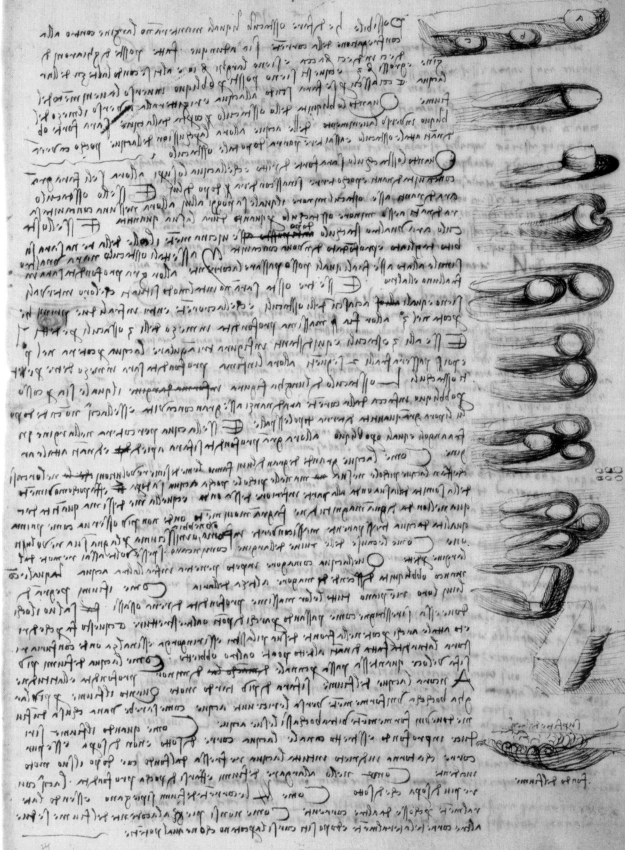

Sheet 14A, folio 23v

This is an elegant page of studies on the physical nature of water, including the explanation of a method to measure the force of a stream of falling water. Leonardo experiments with the physical properties of water, its resistance and cohesion: 'How water has tenacity in itself and cohesion between its particles; this can be seen in its drop which, before it separates from the rest, stretches down as much as it can, holding up at the point of contact until it is overcome by the excessive weight of the water which goes into increasing it.'

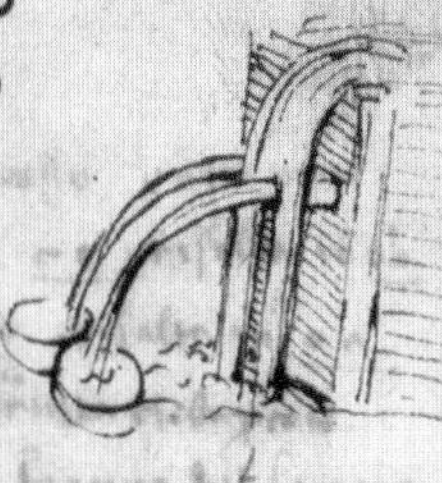

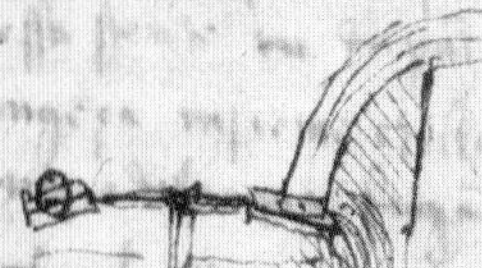

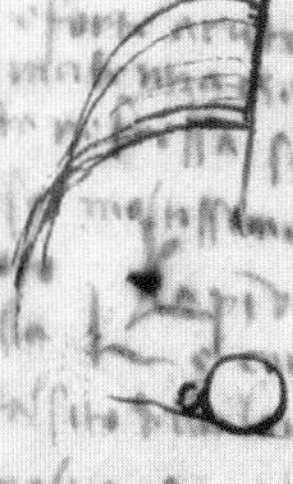

Sheet 14A, folio 14r

This catalogue of twenty-six cases deals with hydrodynamics and the meeting of two or more currents. One of the most interesting pages, it demonstrates how Leonardo's aesthetic and scientific interests are integral to each other. Obstacles are not placed in currents simply to create beautiful stationary patterns. Leonardo observes these effects to find ways to keep river currents from eroding the banks they percuss.

This page includes a comparative discussion of the formation of clouds from water vapour. Leonardo's surprisingly modern concern with friction (*confregazione*) shows his sensitivity to the physics as well as the geometry of water flow.

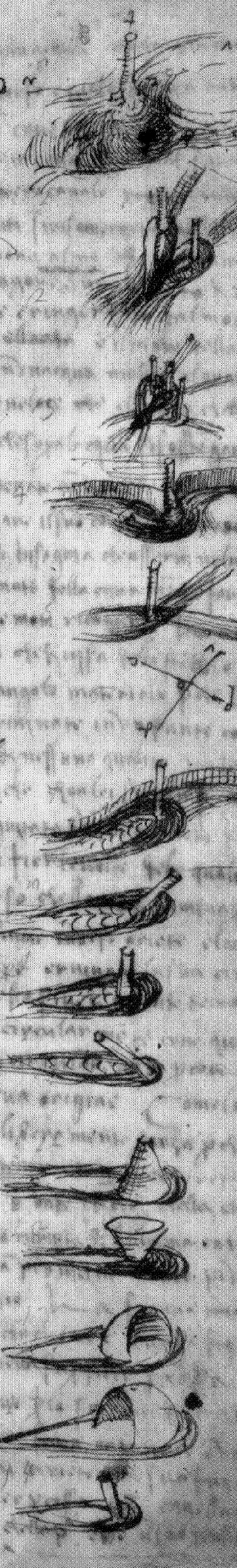

Sheet 14B, folio 14v

Three characteristics of surface waves interest Leonardo here. First, he shows how circular waves can begin in the centre of a round vessel and travel to the edge and back again. Second, he sees how two sets of waves pass through each other without interfering with each other's progress. And third, he describes how a wave, after it strikes a shore, reflects back through its source. He explores these patterns both in nature and under controlled conditions.

Leonardo also records a series of observations on river flow and waterfalls, with detailed descriptions on the type of reflex motions that form eddies. The discussion shifts to wave action and how waves break on shore. Then, through text and diagrams, Leonardo explores the way that surface waves reflect from obstacles but can pass through one another unimpeded.

His observations include how a triangular object dropped into a pond produces waves that quickly acquire a circular form, and the way that circular waves become elongated in a current because water moves forward as well as outward in all directions from the point of impact.

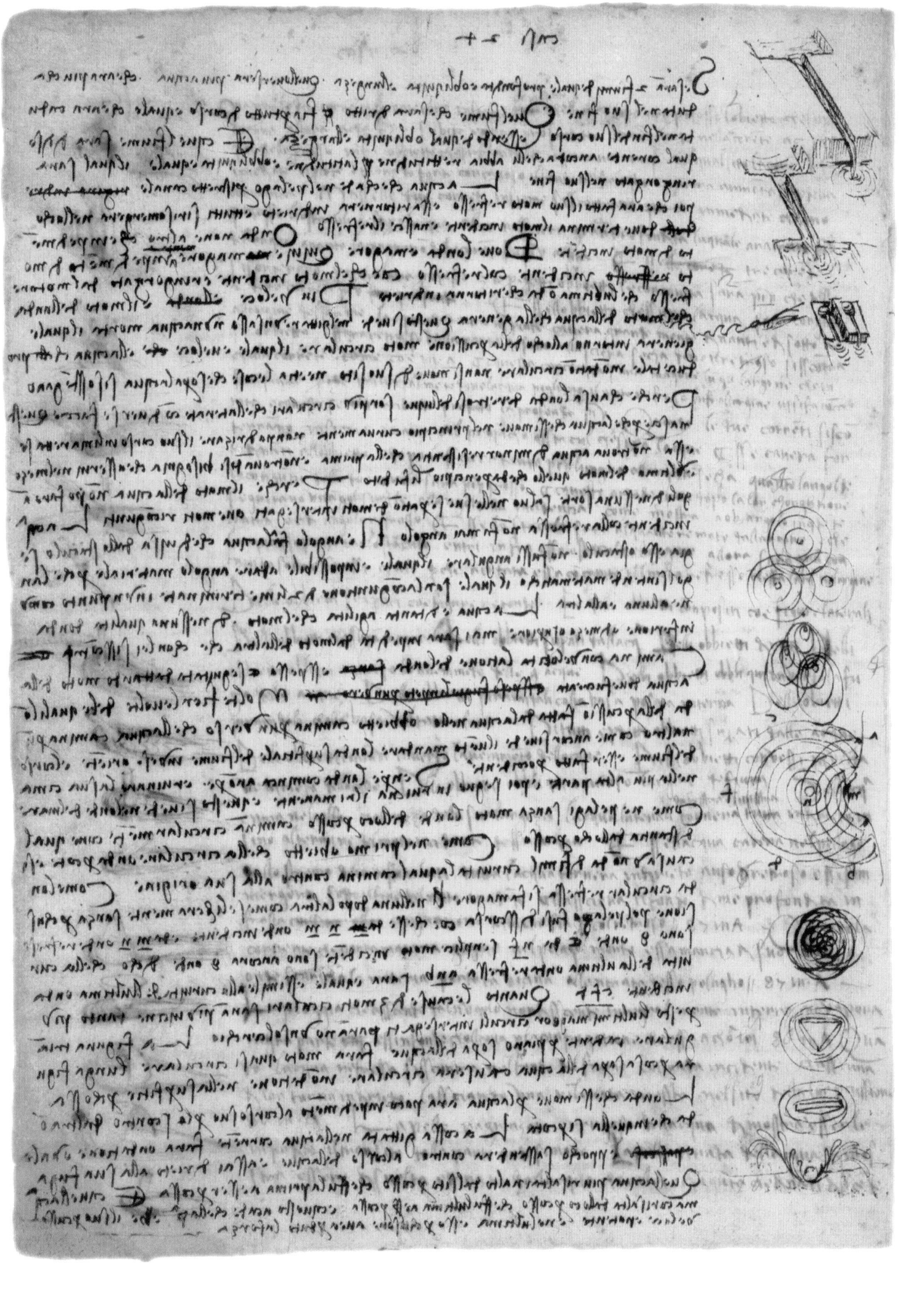

Sheet 14B, folio 23r

This page contains a clear discussion of the basic principle of stationary waves: 'How waves do not penetrate one another, but leap back from the percussed place, and every reflex motion flies away at equal angles from the percussion place.' One of the most innovative aspects of Leonardo's hydraulic interests is revealed in his analysis of the dynamics of fluid flow to maintain stationary waves. This law was not rediscovered by a scientist until 1673, when Christian Huygens formulated the same principle.

Leonardo uses geometry to explain how the intersection points of two expanding circular waves lie on a single line and do not shift off that line as the waves grow. The diagrams here are basic compass constructions requiring only an elementary knowledge of geometry.

The text then shifts back to the general action of waves but transfers them from the element of water to a consideration of how waves of sand form on river bottoms and how waves form in the air. This establishes the validity of the wave principle in three of the four elements.

Leonardo returns the discussion to water, where he began, and notes the basic principle: 'Circular surface waves penetrate one another as impulses, not as a body of water, for the water does not move from its previous place on account of the waves, but only the impulses are transmitted.'

Leonardo's ability to extend the principles he extracts from his observation of the small, such as the surface waves in basins, to the large and back again, as well as from one medium to another, makes the Codex Leicester a unique document. Careful reading reveals that these shifts actually constitute a controlled exploration of the world Leonardo saw around him and his attempts to understand it. Experiments and observations contribute greatly to the ability to synthesise data and search for first principles.

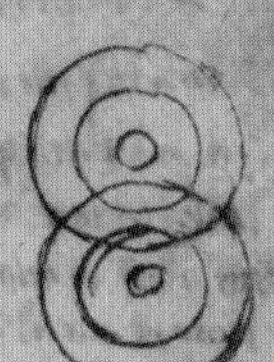

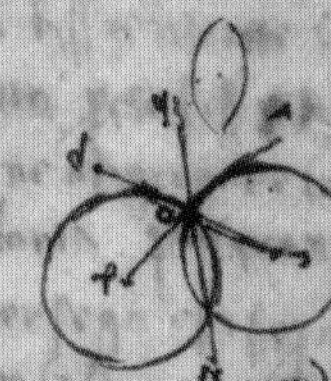
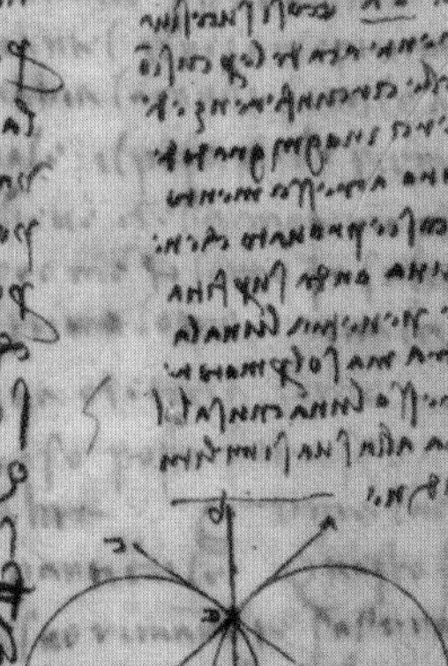

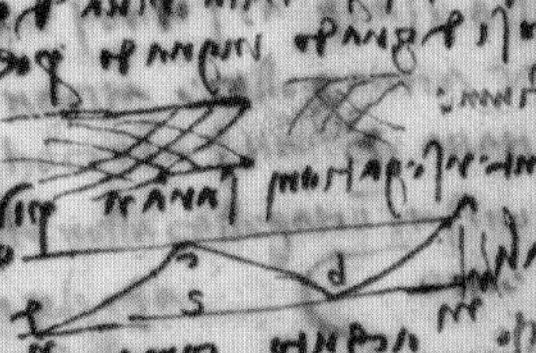

Sheet 15A, folio 22v

One interesting aspect of the codex is the way Leonardo applies his observations of the world around him to practical, or even impractical, devices. While many pages include detailed designs and advice, here a number of quick comments reflect his wide-ranging scrutiny.

Among his ideas for maintaining riverbanks, Leonardo describes how to extend the time a person can remain underwater beyond the duration of a natural breath. He proposes a simple snorkel for breathing underwater. This scientific invention raises a political and moral problem: 'How and why I do not describe my method of remaining underwater for as long a time as I can remain without food; and this I do not publish or divulge on account of the evil nature of men who would practise assassinations at the bottom of the seas by breaking the ships in their lowest parts and sinking them together with the crews who are in them.'

Another part of this page concerns how 'one ought to regulate the impetus of rivers in order to strike terror into the enemy without causing damage to the valleys of a river'.

Leonardo advocates something as simple as swimming lessons for humans and offers advice on how to escape a whirlpool. One should simply 'seek the reflex current that will cast him out of the depths'. A simple solution to the problem of canal silt proposes that 'the bottoms of rivers and ditches are to be trampled by big animals so as to cause muddy waters, which are let out and which will then deposit their soil as they slow down'.

This page also includes some descriptions of the types of natural phenomena that Leonardo used in his artistic studies. The small tornado that he observes on the Arno exhibits the type of whirling drama he employed in studies and the full-scale cartoon for the unrealised painting *The Battle of Anghiari*.

Leonardo's short descriptions of projects and natural phenomena here represent years of observations recorded in small notebooks. All display Leonardo's typical inventiveness and thorough investigation.

Sheet 15A, folio 15r

Leonardo recommends a small experiment with sand to study what happens when streams of differing sizes meet. Where the streams unite, the larger will dam up the smaller. He is also concerned with the way wind penetrates the water to generate whirls.

At the upper right, drawings representing sites where the rivers Rifredi, Mugnone and Ombrone flow into the Arno deal with one of Leonardo's first schemes to regulate and divert the Arno's flow. This project would have redirected the Arno towards Prato and Pistoia. He planned for the new route to go under the mountain pass at Serravalle, an engineering feat of unprecedented scale. He also wanted to transform the huge marshy valley of Chiana into an artificial lake, a retention basin that was to be connected to Lake Trasiveno by means of a tunnel under the hills between Mugnana and San Savino. Leonardo's original plans for the project still exist, including maps, descriptions and even drawings of the excavation machines for constructing the pass.

[illegible]

[illegible]

Sheet 15B, folio 15v

Leonardo works on water current control on this page. He intends to deal with the problem through the placement of various engineered obstacles to redirect flow. In about 1508 Louis XII, the king of France, allowed Leonardo to use a section of the Naviglio Grande Canal in Milan for his hydraulic experiments.

Leonardo sketches complex sets of obstacles in the margins. This series of geometric shapes includes a note expressing a desire to establish a structured study of ways to avoid erosion: 'The science of these objects is of great usefulness, for it teaches how to bend rivers and avoid the ruins of the places percussed by them.'

But obstacles are just part of Leonardo's focus, part of a broader discussion on the control of rivers. The outline for his proposed book on water given here indicates, as does the rest of the manuscript, that Leonardo intended to define the science of water as a deductive one based on first principles and descending from the general to the specific.

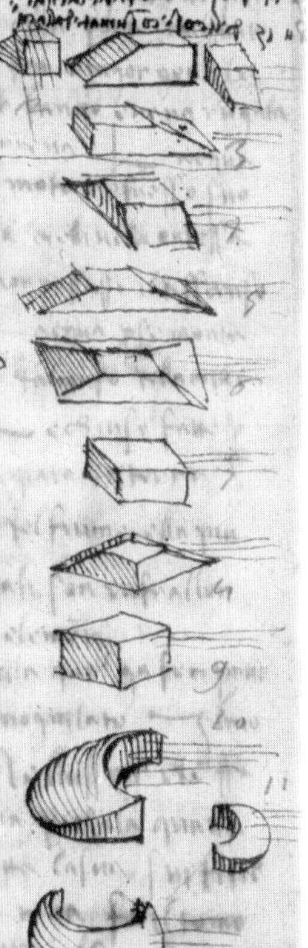

Sheet 15B, folio 22r

The twenty-nine cases of water formation described on this page demonstrate Leonardo's search for principles for his science of water. He acknowledges that weirs may create problems: 'How the impetus of rivers can be controlled by frequent weirs and dams; but this is not useful to the neighbours, because the waters often overflow to inundate their land.'

He also recognises how to mitigate adverse consequences: 'The whirling of the waters reunited after the object which had divided them will circle back towards the percussed obstacle; and so this tortuous motion will proceed, like an auger shell, up to the water surface, always slanting with the water current. Thus, rivers should not have places from which water falls, unless they are in the form of staircase steps, well dovetailed together and chained; and firmly set one on top of the other.'

The symmetry that he sees in eddies studied for the sake of science are elaborated elsewhere in beautiful synthetic drawings of his enduring experience with water.

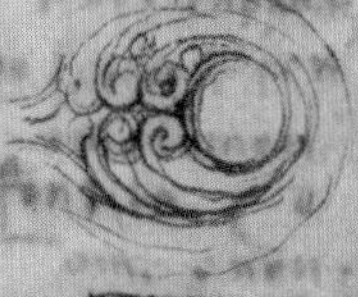

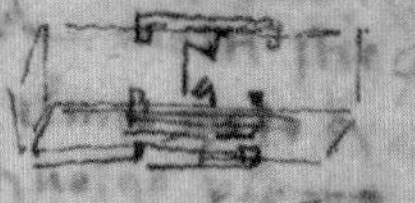

Sheet 16A, folio 21v

Titled 'Conceptions', this page contains ideas for Leonardo's studies of hydraulics as a philosophical inquiry. These ideas include the axiom 'Water of itself does not move unless it descends', as well as references to the spheres of the four elements and a comparison of the circulation system of animals to the body of the earth (the analogy between microcosm and macrocosm). Leonardo uses this basic axiom concerning water's behaviour in a variety of places in this codex to establish a physical link between the water that he observes in minute detail and the universal sphere of water.

On this page, Leonardo presents a paradox: his axiom concerning water flowing downhill is violated by the motion of water within the body of the earth. This break is excused through an analogy with the flow of blood through the body, a mechanism not fully understood in his time. Once the water resumes its natural course over the surface of the earth, however, the basic law resumes its effect: 'When water gushes forth from a burst vein in the earth, it follows the law of other things which are heavier than air, and so always seeks the low places. That water will be swifter which descends by the more slanting line. And that water will be slower which moves along a less slanting bottom.'

Leonardo provides a bridge between the observations of water in the particular, everyday sphere and that which moves in the cosmological framework within which he works intellectually. On folio 25r, he sets up this bridge in the form of a geometric proof. Once that is accomplished, he can explore both the practical and the intellectual implications.

L'acqua per le mortificationi delle montagne. Quell'acqua sarà più alta che sta più remota dal centro della sua sfera. E questa superfitie dell'acqua è tanto più bassa che al centro della sua sfera è più propinqua.

[illegible]

Sheet 16A, folio 16r

On this neatly written page, obviously not the first draft, Leonardo lists '23 propositions' about currents in rivers — basically, an ordering of his ideas with reference to his Libro A, which no longer exists. The propositions concern river islands, currents, waves, and erosion and silt deposition: 'The islands [formed] in rivers will have the heaviest things at the end that faces the oncoming waters rather than at the opposite end. In A, 88.' He discusses how swift water will dig out a river bottom and slow water will fill it up with particulate matter. And 'a small pole fixed at the bottom of a stream will cause a current to hollow out the riverbed for a considerable distance. In A, 74.'

Sheet 16B, folio 16v

A note at the top of this page refers to *On the Flow and Ebb, on Whirlpools and Water*, by Aristotle's student Theophrastus. Leonardo had access to Theophrastus's writings on the history of plants and on characters, because the first edition of his works was published in 1483, with additional editions in 1495 and 1498.

One of the central problems in this codex involves the development of a system of control over the natural movements of rivers and the changes that floods, obstacles, or time may cause in their channels. This page has some of the most practical discussions and observations on this subject, beginning with the first two texts: 'All bridges crumble and collapse towards the oncoming water currents which percuss them above and dig out underneath. All weirs placed diagonally to a river crumble and fall along the rush of the current, away from the oncoming waters, and this because the water flowing over those weirs undermines their foundations.'

Here Leonardo investigates the confluence of rivers, where floods and the interaction of currents may alter the water depth. He studies how both floods and low water influence the deposition of sand and gravel on a riverbed.

The margin illustrations show how obstacles placed in the current can have a great effect on a riverbed and the shape of its bank. Leonardo notes how a current responds to an obstacle placed in a number of basic positions and the changes in response when the structure of the obstacle is altered. It is these responses that Leonardo hopes to take advantage of to control the shifting course and damage of rivers like the Arno.

[illegible]

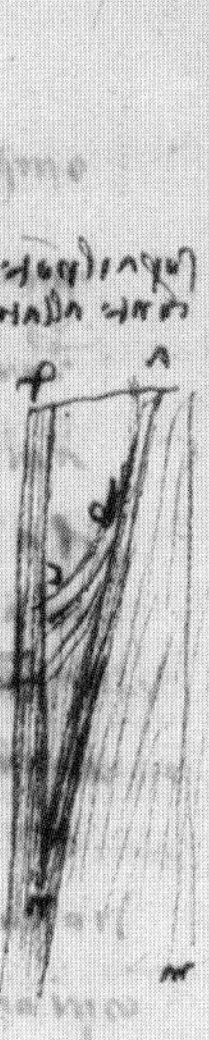

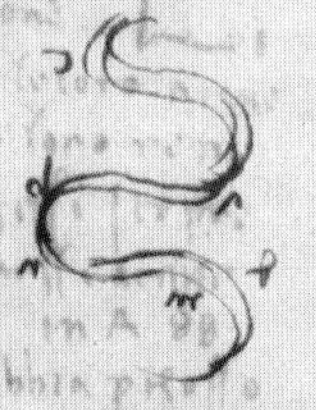

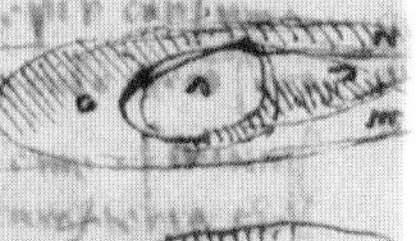

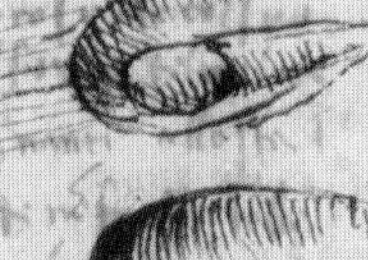

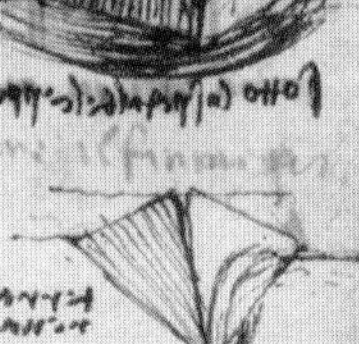

Sheet 16B, folio 21r

Leonardo's elaborate drawings on how to make a durable weir are reminiscent of the beautiful drawings of machines in the Codex Madrid I. The energy he expended on practical applications of his study of water remind us that many waterways — a whole network of inland canals — were under construction during Leonardo's lifetime. He was influenced by the visible remains of a twelfth-century canal network in Lombardy. Leonardo, however, was the first person to theorise about the flow of water he observed. We can chart the emergence of his interests through drawings of machines in the Codex Madrid I, based on a scheme by Heron of Alexandria. He could have known Heron's work in manuscript, in Commandino's Latin translation or, most likely, through the translation of his friend and fellow engineer Francesco di Giorgio Martini.

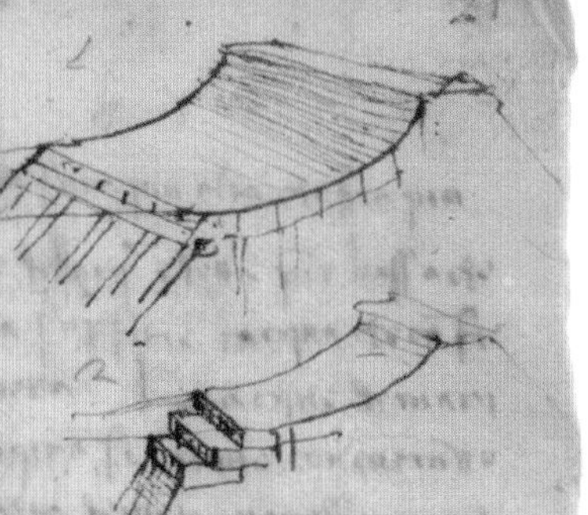

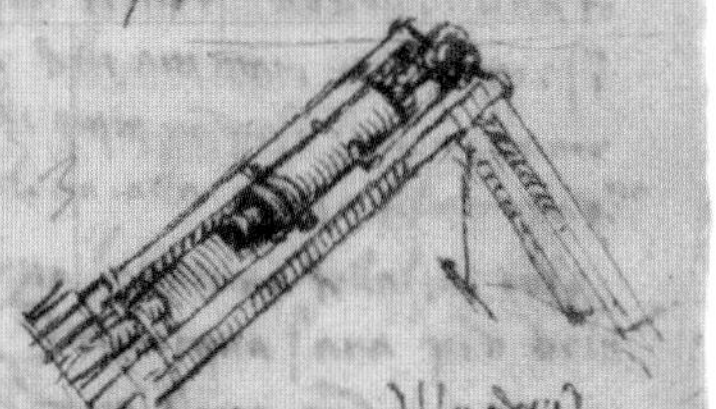

Sheet 17A, folio 20v

The continuing discussion of the confluence of currents around obstructions and what causes circular wave patterns focuses in particular on what happens to river bottoms and banks.

The first half of this page considers the nature of flowing water in relation to the subject of dams, with indications of possible weak and dangerous breaking points. These Leonardo details in illustrations: 'A water current which carries matter often turns itself, together with that matter, into a bank and an obstacle to its straight course; thus it deflects and breaks sideways at the weaker point … which brings about a new deflection as the obstacle is broken at its weakest point, and so it goes on successively.'

Next Leonardo examines the presence of obstacles on the beds of flowing waters and their effect on bottom sand and deep currents: 'The obstacles produced by the movement of the water on its bottom move on slowly after the swift course of the waters because the water which percusses them moves the sand from the bottom of such a hill to its top … and the heavier parts … run down the opposite side of the hill … and having reached the foot of the hill, here it stops.'

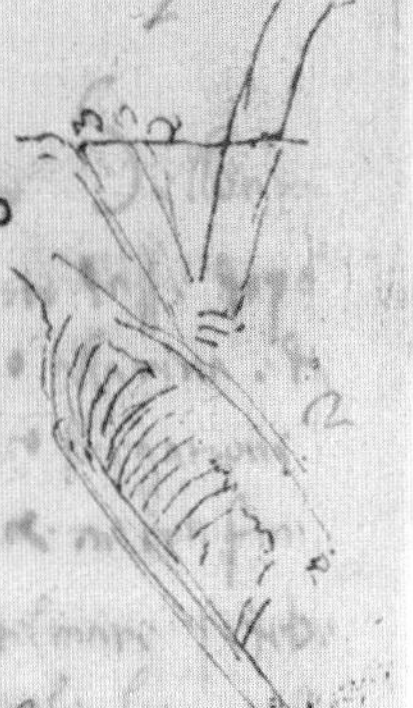

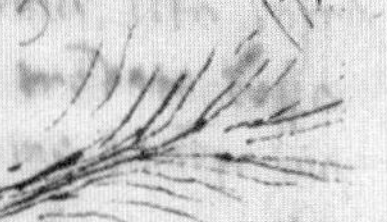

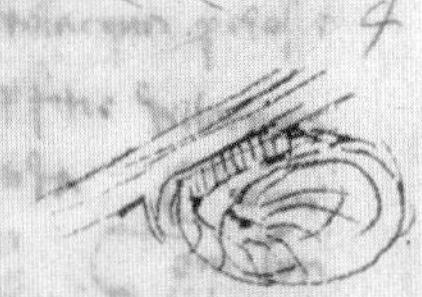

Sheet 17A, folio 17r

Here Leonardo discusses the sediment carried by rivers and where various kinds of this sediment are deposited. He also records ideas for draining swamps, for which his expertise was frequently sought. The writing has the flavour of a technical manual for hydraulic engineers. It is a far cry from his philosophical musings or evocative poetic descriptions about the body of the earth found elsewhere in the codex.

Leonardo rarely makes sketches within the text, preferring to illustrate his major points in the outer margin with substantiating explanations. This page, with its interspersed drawings directly referring to specific notes, is an exception. His margin here contains only one reference and illustration, on the method for draining a swamp.

The presence of silt or other detritus radically affects the flow of water. Leonardo extrapolates, case by case: 'How clear waters which enter into swamps cause their waters to lower — that is, by removing soil from their bottom. How waters taken from swamps in order to dry them ought to be taken when the tide causes the sea level to drop. How narrow entrances and exits in great lakes cause the soil carried by turbid waters to be deposited in these lakes. How wide entrances and exits in lakes cause the soil to be removed, making such lakes deeper. How a turbid river which pours into a swamp fills up and dries this swamp.'

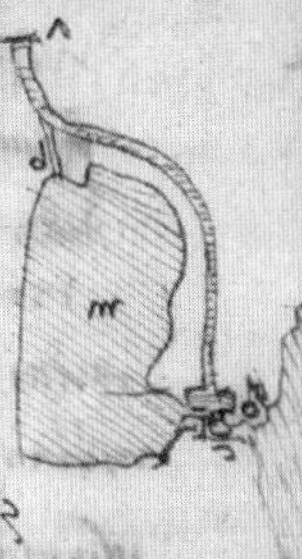

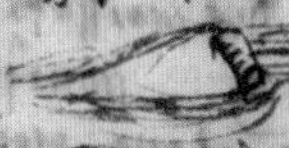

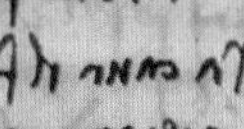

Sheet 17B, folio 17v

This page is an important document for the study of Leonardo's organisation of a treatise dedicated to the science of water. He begins with general concerns, moves to the specific, and indicates that he intends to found a new, deductive science based on first principles. On this page, Leonardo considers 'whether flow and ebb are caused by the moon or the sun, or they are the breathing of this machine, the earth'.

Later thoughts on the same subject are recorded in Paris Manuscript E (circa 1513–14) and Paris Manuscript F. Interestingly, his outline for the treatise includes very little on waves and nothing on rivers, two of his greatest interests in the Codex Leicester.

This unillustrated page contains further observations on the nature of water. Leonardo here seems motivated by a longing to understand water's behaviours beyond the mere observation and recording of data. His pure science is tempered by doubt and premonition.

ordine de libro delle acque [illegible]

[illegible]

Sheet 17B, folio 20r

This page, full of Leonardo's thoughts, notes, meditations and poetic ruminations, ranges over a wide area of subject matter connected with his considerations of the body of the earth and his field studies of water. He questions 'whether the movement of the wind is curved, according to the curvature of the watery sphere, or rectilinear'.

Leonardo offers a vision of the distant future of the Mediterranean basin, when it will be reduced to a single river: 'How the Mediterranean seas will lay bare their depths to the air and will only keep the channel of the greatest river that flows there, which will run to the ocean and there discharge its waters together with those of all the rivers that are its tributaries.'

Leonardo continues with seeming quandaries over natural phenomena, such as the flooding of the Adige and the great plagues: 'Why the Adige rises every seven years and falls every seven years, and is the cause of famine or abundance. Why following great pestilences the rivers are made deeper and run clear, and previously they were wide and of but little depth and always turbid.'

Almost immediately, Leonardo shifts gears and moves on to reassuring observations on the colour of air that directly relate to his painting: 'How the brightness of the atmosphere is caused by the water that is dissolved in it and that has formed itself into imperceptible particles which, after taking the light of the sun from the opposite side, give back the brightness that is visible in the atmosphere; and the blue that appears in it is caused by the darkness which is hidden behind this atmosphere.'

Leonardo's prose conveys a feeling of the encyclopaedic range of his planned treatise rather than a research proposal.

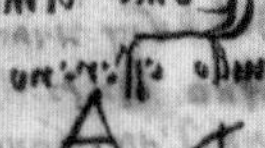

Sheet 18A, folio 19v

Leonardo's thirty-seven cases of general observations deal with the viscosity of water in relation to its velocity and to deposits left by various kinds of particles carried in the water. The subject matter includes rain water, spurts of water and rivers: 'Rain water is lighter than other waters, and more so in winter than in summer because it does not mix with dust in the air as it does in summer. Clear sea water is heavier than turbid fresh water because salt is heavier than earth. A river of greater slant will thrust its waters underneath those of a river of lesser slant. A spout of rising water is higher in the centre than at the edges.'

These and other highly evolved, technical discussions recorded on this page reflect Leonardo's many years of field experience as a hydraulic engineer. Observations about riverbeds, gravel, stones and sand continue in a similar fashion on the facing page, folio 18r.

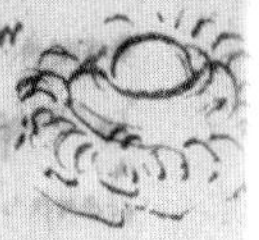

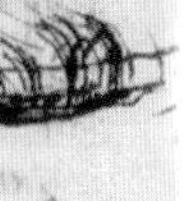

Sheet 18A, folio 18r

Titled '32 cases', this page principally deals with flowing water, most of it falling or reflecting. It also contains practical observations made with a confidence based on experience.

The last line, 'How the fire of Mongibello [Mount Etna in Sicily] is fed thousands of miles away from its mouth', suggests that Leonardo was pondering the problem of the body of the earth when he first recorded his ideas.

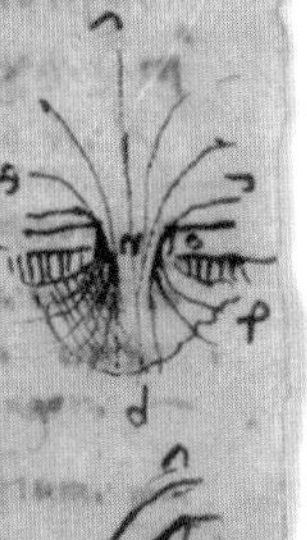

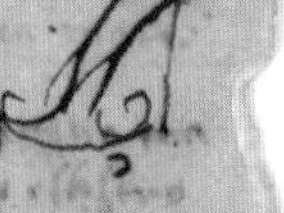

Sheet 18B, folio 18v

The subject of this page is the meeting of two rivers, one large and the other smaller. Leonardo makes some intricate visual analyses of the deposits and wave patterns that result from their confluence. He mentions Mensola and the Arno, and from this we can infer that Leonardo recorded his thoughts while he was actively working on a grand canalisation project.

His first conclusion concerns mud and sand: 'When a lesser river flows into a greater river, the lesser river dams up its own waters, which, as they slow down, receive large quantities of mud and sand carried by the velocity of the greater river, and this greater river deposits them there because in slowing down it cannot keep them afloat.'

Leonardo's confluence studies result in very practical applications.

Sheet 18B, folio 19r

This is another page strictly concerned with Leonardo's professional activities as a hydraulic engineer. The most interesting facet, perhaps, is his concern with the effects of friction (*confregazione*) of physical materials in the action of water. It is instructive to compare these findings with his study of incidence and reflection in light, where no mass is involved and friction is therefore not an issue.

Here Leonardo makes it clear that the angle of rebound is always less than the angle of incidence because the mass loses power on impact with the foreign surface. 'The incident and reflex motions of the waters are never rectilinear, nor do they occur between equal angles, because the angle of reflection is wider than that of incidence; and this is because reflected rays bend as they are impeded by the river current, over which they cross each other, which percusses them and bends them towards the end of the river.'

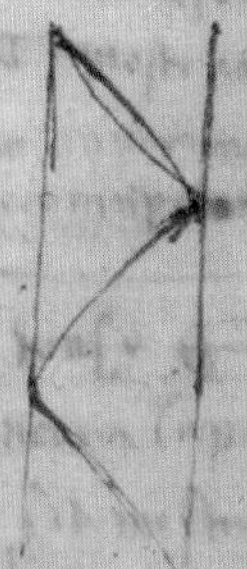

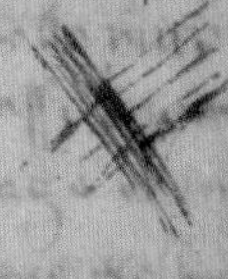

FURTHER READING

Pedretti, Carlo. *Leonardo da Vinci on painting: a lost book (Libro A) reassembled from the Codex Vaticanus Urbinas 1270 and from the Codex Leicester*, Peter Owen, London, 1965.

Freud, Sigmund. *Leonardo da Vinci and a memory of his childhood*; tr Alan Tyson, W W Norton, New York, 1964.

Wallace, Robert. *The world of Leonardo, 1452–1511,* Time Inc, New York, 1966.

Kemp, Martin. *Leonardo da Vinci: the marvellous works of nature and man*, Dent, London, 1981.

Brizio, Anna Maria, Brugnoli, Maria Vittoria and Chastel, André. *Leonardo the artist,* McGraw Hill, New York, 1980.

Wasserman, Jack. *Leonardo*, Harry N Abrams, New York, 1984.

Leonardo on painting: an anthology of writings, ed Martin Kemp, Yale University Press, New Haven, 1989.

Clark, Kenneth. *Leonardo da Vinci,* Penguin, Harmondsworth, 1993.

Pedretti, Carlo. *Leonardo da Vinci nature studies from the Royal Library at Windsor Castle*, exhibition catalogue, Art Gallery of New South Wales, Sydney, 1984.

Pedretti, Carlo. *Leonardo, architect*, tr Sue Brill, Rizzoli, New York, 1985.

ABOUT THE POWERHOUSE MUSEUM

The Powerhouse Museum is Australia's largest and most popular museum. Established in 1880, it is a museum of decorative arts, design, science, technology and social history with a collection that encompasses Australian and international, historical and contemporary material culture. In 1988 the museum moved into new premises, a refurbished power station.

The mission of the Powerhouse Museum is to inspire diverse audiences by using the collection and scholarship to provide informative and innovative exhibitions, programs and services. The Powerhouse Museum has a reputation for quality and excellence in collecting, preserving and presenting aspects of world cultures for present and future generations.